3/03

WRESTLING

STRENGTH

THE COMPETITIVE EDGE

Matt Brzycki

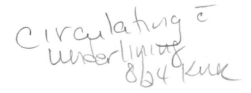

a RAM Publishing Pruduction
Blue River Press, Indianapolis, Indiana

LCCN: 2002091009

Cover designed by Phil Velikan
Cover photography courtesy of Lanny Bryant, *Wrestling USA* magazine

Printed in the United States of America
10 9 8 7 6 5 4 3 2 1

Distributed in the United States by
Cardinal Publishers Group
7301 Georgetown Road, Suite 118
Indianapolis, Indiana 46268
www.cardinalpub.com

TABLE OF CONTENTS

PREFACE

From February 1986-May 2001, I have had nearly 60 articles featured in *Wrestling USA* magazine. I would like to thank Lanny Bryant and his family for publishing those articles in their magazine and granting permission to allow them to be compiled in book form.

The articles were written over the course of more than 15 years, the earliest appearing in the February 15, 1986 issue. I have done some editing of the articles for this book to "standardize" the changes in my style of writing that have occurred over this lengthy period of time. Actually, all of the articles that I wrote prior to 1991 were done on a typewriter. As you might imagine, it was quite painstaking to make any changes to the text. In fact, making the smallest of changes required retyping sections of the article or, in some cases, the entire article. Needless to say, the texts of those early articles were essentially rough "first drafts" and I have used this opportunity to make belated edits.

Though I never competed as a wrestler, the sport of wrestling has given me a wealth of fond memories. My earliest recollection dates back to when I was a young teen who marveled at — and was inspired by — the renowned physical training of the great Dan Gable as he prepared for the 1972 Olympics in Munich. Another memory that I have of wrestlers is from 1978. At the time, I was a 21-year-old Drill Instructor at the Marine Corps Recruit Depot in San Diego, California. As part of their training, recruits had to maneuver through an obstacle course that consisted of numerous poles, logs, beams and hurdles and ended with a rope climb. Negotiating the obstacle course in a speedy fashion requires a high degree of strength, balance, agility and determination. As motivation, recruits were timed in their efforts and a record was kept for the best-ever time. Every now and then, a recruit would break the all-time record by a half second or so. One day, word quickly spread about a recruit who broke the record for the obstacle course by an unbelievable two seconds. The depot newspaper ran an article about the recruit who set the new record — an unusually large individual who had gone to college on a football scholarship and later joined the Marines. To make a long story short, the recruit was Greg Gibson. He went on to become a three-time world silver medalist in freestyle wrestling from 1981-83 and the 1984 Olympic silver medalist in Greco-Roman wrestling. (At the time of this writing, Greg was a Master Sergeant in the Marine Corps and assistant coach of their wrestling team.) In 1981 as an undergraduate student at Penn State, I participated in a wrestling class taught by the legendary Bill Koll who was a three-time NCAA champion for Northern Iowa (1946-48) and twice won the award as the outstanding wrestler in the tournament (1947-48). Despite his age, we still dreaded having him demonstrate moves on us. Among other things, we did not want to be on the wrong end of a cross face.

Of all the different sports with which I have worked over the years, I have been with wrestling the longest and on the most regular basis. Since September 1982, I have been involved in the strength and conditioning of collegiate wrestlers at three different schools: Penn State, Princeton University and Rutgers University. Over this period of time, I have met a great number of wrestlers and coaches who have meant much to me both professionally as well as personally. From a professional standpoint, I have had the opportunity to work with two of the all-time coaching greats in the history of collegiate wrestling: John Johnston of Princeton and Deane Oliver of Rutgers — both of whom were head coaches at the collegiate level for a total of more than a half century (and they themselves were accomplished collegiate wrestlers as well). In addition, I have worked with hundreds of their wrestlers (and those of John Johnston's two very capable coaching successors, Eric Pearson and Michael

New) who are far too numerous to mention. From a personal standpoint, the best man at my wedding was Andy Foltiny who wrestled for Rutgers in the late 1970s (captaining the team as a senior) and then served as an assistant wrestling coach at the school for more than a decade. Andy was also my training partner from 1985 - 90 and, pound-for-pound, was one of the strongest men that I have ever seen. And several years ago, Tom O'Rourke — another exceptionally strong individual who wrestled for Andy at Rutgers (also captaining the team as a senior) — asked me to be the godfather of his daughter, Kathleen.

Wrestlers quickly gained my utmost respect primarily because of their warrior-like nature. Like true warriors, wrestlers are generally fierce, relentless, intense, aggressive, dedicated, resourceful and purposeful to a degree that separates them from most others. Boxers, judo players and the various martial artists are also true warriors. Unfortunately, the fact of the matter is that the warrior is a vanishing breed.

As a sport, you cannot get much more basic than wrestling. There is really no equipment except for the uniform — and there is very little of that. There are no implements or apparatus. It is just a wrestler and an opponent. Two warriors. One goal.

This book is dedicated to wrestlers and the warrior lifestyle.

Matt Brzycki
May 2, 2002

Chapter 1
CONVENTIONAL STRENGTH TRAINING

Milo . . . Hercules . . . Sandow . . . Anderson . . . Kazmaier . . . Schwarzenegger . . . Suleymanoglu . . . Superman. Some are real while a few are imaginary. Nevertheless, all of them are legendary for their feats of strength. In the early 1970s, several universities and professional teams began to realize the importance of strength training and, therefore, sought advice from individuals who appeared to be well versed in this area. This professional became known as the "strength coach." Traditionally, strength coaches have been chosen from the ranks of the competitive weightlifters — that is, the Olympic-style lifters, the powerlifters and occasionally the bodybuilders. This was only natural since competitive lifters seem to exemplify the highest levels of strength and health. After all, they can lift a lot of weight and generally have decent physiques, right?

The problem arises when strength coaches elect to train their athletes like competitive weightlifters. (For the record, I am a former competitive powerlifter.) Naturally, many strength coaches advocate programs that are familiar to them. Generally, these are programs that they themselves used as competitive weightlifters. As a result, many athletes are now using weightlifting programs under the guise of weight-training programs. This is frequently referred to as "traditional" or "conventional" strength training.

Contrary to popular belief, the differences between weight training and weightlifting are more than just semantics. The main purpose of weight training is to reduce your athletes' potential for injury while the second purpose is to increase your athletes' performance potential. But make no mistake about it, weight training is primarily an injury-prevention service.

9

Weight training involves a relatively low volume of activity. It is most often typified by brief sessions of high-intensity exercise performed 2-3 times per week. In general, one or two exercises are designated for the major muscle groups of the body. Each exercise is performed for a prescribed number of repetitions, usually 15-20 for the hips, 10-15 for the legs and 6-12 for the upper body. Repetitions are done throughout a full range of motion in a deliberate, controlled manner.

On the other hand, weightlifting — or conventional strength training — involves a relatively high volume of activity. It is characterized by multiple sets of low-repetition movements performed as many as six times per week. The ultimate goal of weightlifting is to lift as much weight as possible for one repetition. The conventional strength program usually emphasizes the movements that are performed in competition by weightlifters: the clean and jerk, snatch, squat, bench press and deadlift. From these basic lifts a number of generic offspring have been conceived such as the power clean, squat clean, push press, push jerk, power pull, snatch pull, hang clean pull and others. These movements generally make up the so-called "core exercises" of a weightlifting program. Moreover, the ability to lift heavy weights for a one-repetition maximum is often used as a barometer to measure potential achievement in the athletic arena. Finally, the repetitions are performed in a rapid, explosive fashion.

AREAS OF CONCERN

Conventional strength programs have several areas of major concern that should be addressed in greater detail:

Power Clean et al.

The power clean. Many coaches swear by it; many athletes swear at it. Arguably, it is the one exercise most often associated with the conventional strength program. For decades, this movement has been used in an attempt to mimic certain explosive sports skills with the belief that there will be a positive transfer of motor ability to the athletic arena. Unfortunately, there is absolutely no evidence in the motor-learning literature to suggest that power cleans will make you more explosive or otherwise

BOOYA!

"carry over" to the performance of other sports movements. Furthermore, there is no exercise done in the weight room — with barbells or machines — that will have a direct impact on perfecting a given sports skill or cause athletes to become more explosive. Power cleans will only improve your ability to do power cleans, barbell squats will only improve your ability to do barbell squats and so on. Therefore, many athletes are spending needless time and energy learning useless competitive-lifting techniques.

There is no question that this and other movements used by competitive weightlifters can be productive for increasing strength. The biggest concern, however, lies in their inherent risk of injury. Most of the exercises performed by competitive weightlifters expose the muscles, joints and connective tissue to excessive forces that can result in numerous traumatic injuries or predispose an athlete to later injuries.

Studies have suggested that weightlifters may be prone to developing spondylolysis. That was one of the conclusions drawn by the American Orthopedic Society for Sports Medicine. During an interview dealing with a published study, a medical doctor stated, "We believe that spondylolysis represents a mechanical failure caused by the overload of competitive lifts." He continued by specifically mentioning the clean and jerk, the snatch and the deadlift.

In 1984, newspapers published two shocking photographs of weightlifters who competed in the Los Angeles Olympics. In one photo, a West German lifter — Manfred Nerlinger — appeared to be doing the limbo with a loaded barbell. In reality, he slipped and lost control of the barbell during the initial phase of the clean and jerk. (The initial phase is essentially a power clean.) The photo showed him a split second before he landed on his back with the barbell on his chest. Miraculously, he was able to walk away uninjured. The other photo featured an American lifter — middleweight Derrick Crass — who was not quite that lucky. In the photo, he was shown hitting his head with the bar while his right shoulder and elbow were bent at a grotesque angle. In the aftermath, the lifter collapsed to the platform and remained laying there for several minutes. Eventually, he had to be carried away. The lifter suffered a dislocated right elbow and a strained right knee. Hey, these guys were highly skilled weightlifters who practiced perfecting their techniques for countless hours. Indeed, Mr. Nerlinger actually won the bronze medal at those Olympics and, at the time, Mr. Crass was the best weightlifter in the United States at his bodyweight. Are we going to train our athletes with these movements when the potential for traumatic injury is so obvious? The risk certainly seems unjustified to me.

Barbell Squat

Barbell squats are yet another frightful story. Besides causing excessive sheer forces in the knee joint, placing a weighted barbell on the shoulders results in compression of the spinal column. This is most evident in the bottom position of the barbell squat, where the anterior aspect of the lumbar vertebrae is compressed. This pushes the intervertebral disks in posterior direction and could result in a herniated or ruptured disk. In fact, research has revealed electromyographical activity of 6-10 times bodyweight in the lumbar region when squatting with as little as about 1-1½ times bodyweight. Again, this is another movement that seems to invite injuries rather than prevent them.

SUMMING IT UP

Recently, I received a letter from a wrestling coach from Wisconsin who has 18 years of coaching experience. The coach stated that he has read numerous articles on weight training but noticed that there were many differences of opinion. He added that this can lead to a great deal of confusion. After all, what is right? More importantly, what is wrong? As coaches, it is our task to read information critically and determine what is the most efficient, productive, practical and safest way to train our athletes.

For example, most of the exercises used by competitive lifters can certainly be productive. However, many of the movements can also be destructive. Therefore, your athletes should not train like weightlifters. Coaches who advocate potentially dangerous exercises are doing a disservice to their athletes and also may be setting up themselves for a lawsuit.

Chapter 2
A PRACTICAL APPROACH

It is generally agreed upon that strength training represents a valuable means of reducing the likelihood of injury as well as increasing performance potential. However, confusion arises when we, as coaches, must decide on what type of strength system to implement. As coaches, we are inundated with the "latest" information on strength and conditioning via magazines, books, research studies and personal anecdotes. Some of this material is productive, efficient and safe but, unfortunately, much of it is unreasonable, inefficient and sometimes dangerous. As a matter of fact, some types of training can be downright destructive.

Though there is no "one best method" of training, some are better than others. As a competitive powerlifter, I typically spent 3-4 hours per workout in the weight room performing countless sets of low-repetition movements at a correspondingly low level of intensity. Although this type of training was somewhat productive for demonstrating strength, there are more practical ways for building strength. Moreover, low-repetition movements done with heavy resistance are potentially dangerous. Finally, it was obviously inefficient in terms of time and would certainly be impractical — if not impossible — for training large numbers of athletes.

THE GUIDELINES

Athletes need not — and should not — spend large amounts of time strength training. A program should be incorporated which will stimulate the maximal possible gains in the least amount of time. This type of program is increasingly popular

13

and is used by numerous collegiate and professional teams to train their athletes.

The following guidelines will aid a coach in organizing a practical strength program that is safe, efficient and productive:

Intensity

Except for genetics, this is probably the most important factor for achieving maximal results from strength training. In order to obtain the greatest possible results, research suggests that you must train with a high level of intensity (or effort). The harder you train, the better your response. The only way that you will know your level of effort is high enough is to lift a weight to the point of momentary muscular fatigue. In other words, your wrestlers should perform each prescribed exercise until they literally cannot do any more repetitions. A sub-maximal effort will give them a sub-maximal response.

Progression

In order for a muscle to get stronger, you must force it to do progressively harder work. Therefore, every time your athletes work out, encourage them to increase the weight, repetitions or both. Stressing your muscles in this manner will cause them to adapt by increasing in size and strength. Each time your athletes attain the maximal number of prescribed repetitions, have them increase the resistance by about 5% or less.

Sets

Your athletes need only perform one set of each exercise but each set must be a maximal effort. One all-out set done to the point of momentary muscular fatigue will be the metabolic equivalent of several sub-maximal sets. Multiple sets are relatively inefficient in terms of time and, therefore, are unnecessary.

Repetitions

There is absolutely no conclusive research that suggests low repetitions will "bulk up" muscles and high repetitions will "tone" muscles. Your athletes' responses to strength training are based upon their genetics and are not subject to change.

14

In general, most individuals should reach momentary muscular fatigue within 15-20 repetitions (or 90-120 seconds) when training the hips, 10-15 repetitions (or 60-90 seconds) for the rest of the lower body and 6-12 repetitions (or 40-70 seconds) for the upper torso. This can be followed immediately by 2-4 post-fatigue repetitions.

Some people — because of their genetic makeup — may require a slightly higher repetition range in order to maximize their response to exercise. For example, some individuals possess a higher percentage of the so-called "fast-twitch" (FT) muscle fibers than most people. These muscle fibers can generate a lot of force but have a very low endurance capacity. These individuals would probably benefit more from strength training by using a slightly lower repetition range since their predominant muscle fibers tend to limit their endurance somewhat. Approximate ranges of 10-15 for the hips, 9-12 for the rest of the lower body and 6-8 for the upper torso would probably yield better results. On the other hand, some individuals are predominantly "slow twitch" (ST). Compared to the FT fibers, ST fibers cannot generate as much force but have greater endurance. Therefore, those individuals who possess a high percentage of ST fibers would be more successful using slightly higher ranges such as about 20-25 for the hips, 15-20 for the legs and 10-15 for the upper body.

The only way to positively determine your predominant fiber type is by analyzing a sample of your muscle tissue under a microscope. However, you can sometimes make a logical guess based upon your athletes' abilities. Those who are reasonably successful at sports which require them to generate a lot of force in a short amount of time are probably more FT and should use slightly lower repetitions; those who seem to be more successful at endurance activities are probably more ST and should use slightly higher repetitions. In any event, the previously suggested ranges still serve as excellent guidelines for mostly everyone.

Weight

Have your wrestlers use a weight that will cause them to reach momentary muscular fatigue within their prescribed repetition range. If muscular fatigue occurs before they reach their repetition range, the weight is too heavy and should be reduced for their next workout. Likewise, if they exceed the upper level of their repetition range before experiencing muscular fatigue, the weight is too light and should be increased for their next workout.

Form

Have your athletes exercise throughout the greatest possible range of motion (ROM) that safety allows. This will increase your athletes' flexibility thereby reducing their potential for injury. Additionally, exercising throughout a full ROM will stimulate the maximal number of muscle fibers and result in greater strength gains.

Require your wrestlers to raise and lower the weight in a deliberate, controlled manner. It should take about 1-2 seconds to raise the weight and 3-4 seconds to lower it. This will decrease the likelihood of incurring an injury while strength training. Furthermore, it will ensure that their muscles are doing most of the work instead of momentum. In short, strength training will be safer and more efficient by using strict form.

Duration

More is better when it comes to knowledge and happiness; more is not better when it comes to strength training. An inverse relationship exists between time and intensity. As the length of your activity increases, your intensity must decrease. Therefore, if your athletes are training with a high level of intensity, they literally cannot work for a long period of time. Generally, a workout should take no more than about one hour.

Volume

A workout should consist of about 17-19 total exercises. The focal point for most of these exercises should be the hips, legs and upper torso. Include one exercise for the hips, hamstrings, quadriceps, lower legs, biceps, triceps, lower arms, abdominals and lower back; select two exercises for the chest, upper back and shoulders. A workout should also include 2-4 neck exercises. Occasionally, your athletes may want to perform an additional movement to emphasize a particular body part. That's okay as long as they continue to make progressions in weight and/or repetitions.

Sequence

Whenever possible, have your wrestlers work their muscles from largest to smallest: hips, upper legs (hamstrings and quadriceps), lower legs (calves or dorsi flexors), upper torso (chest, upper back and shoulders), upper arms (biceps and triceps), lower arms (forearms), abdominals and lower back. Although it violates the "largest-to-smallest" rule, it is best to exercise the neck at the beginning of the routine while you are still fresh mentally and physically.

Frequency

At most, your athletes should do three total-body workouts per week (every other day). Your muscles require about a 48- to 72-hour recovery period between workouts in order to get stronger. Performing any more than three total-body sessions in a week can be counterproductive and you will soon reach a catabolic or "overtrained" state.

After about 96 hours without a strength workout, your muscles will begin to get progressively weaker. That is why it is important to continue strength training even while in-season or when competing. However, you will need to reduce your workouts to twice a week due to the increased activity level of practices and meets. One session should be done the day after your meet and another no sooner than 48 hours before your next meet.

Records

It is extremely important that your athletes keep accurate records of the date, weight, repetitions and order of exercise. A workout card is your way of monitoring the progress of your wrestlers in the weight room.

Supervision

This is probably a coach's most important function in the weight room since it ensures that the athletes are following the

11 previous guidelines. Proper supervision is also necessary to provide a safe environment in which your athletes can train.

SUMMING IT UP

Remember that "weight training" differs from "weight lifting." Many weightlifting movements can be damaging to your musculoskeletal system. Do not get caught up in the "numbers game" by emphasizing how much weight your athletes can lift. The winner of a wrestling match has never been decided by a bench-press contest. Weight training also differs from bodybuilding. The purpose of bodybuilding is to develop the body as much as possible. There is nothing wrong with wanting to look better. But do not forget, you could look like Tarzan and still wrestle like Cheetah!

According to one strength coach, "Weight training is done to prevent injury. Anything else is a plus." Indeed, your athletes should be lifting weight to increase their functional strength. Brief sessions of high-intensity exercise using a progressive overload represent a practical way of meeting this objective in a safe, productive and efficient manner.

Chapter 3
THE "TWENTY-HOUR RULE:"
A STRENGTH COACH'S PERSPEC-
TIVE

The 85th National Collegiate Athletic Association (NCAA) Convention adopted a new regulation that governs all sports. It became effective on August 1, 1991 for every Division I and II school and will become effective on August 1, 1992 for all Division III programs. Officially, the rule is designated in the *1991-92 NCAA Manual* by the decimal number 17.1.5 and by the topic subsection of "Time Limits for Athletically Related Activities." Essentially, the new rule states that during the playing season "a student-athlete's participation in countable athletically related activities shall be limited to a maximum of 4 hours per day and 20 hours per week." During the season, athletes must also receive at least one day off per week. When out of season, a student-athlete's participation in permissible activities is limited to a maximum of eight hours per week. In the coaching community, this recent legislation is often referred to as the "Twenty-Hour Rule." Regardless of the name, its content will have an immediate and major impact on the time that collegiate athletes are involved in their chosen sport.

With the current restrictions on the number of hours that an athlete is permitted to spend in sports-related activities, there will be a new emphasis on "quality time." More than ever before, coaches will try to produce the maximal possible results in the minimum amount of time. "Quality" and "efficiency" will be the latest buzzwords for those activities that are considered "athletically related." These activities include practices, coach-initiated meetings on athletic matters, required individual workouts and supervised videotape/film reviews of athletic performance. In addition, coaches will be searching for a time-efficient means of administering strength and conditioning programs to their athletes. Indeed, instead of being concerned with the *quantity* of work done in the weight room, coaches will be emphasizing the *quality* of work done in the weight room. Let's face it, gone are the days when a coach "encouraged" an athlete to lift 4-6 days per week for two hours or more per session. And those hours did not even count some type of conditioning activity.

How can we make strength workouts more time-efficient without sacrificing results? Well, let's look at what is needed to increase muscular strength. In order to increase in size and strength, you have to fatigue the muscle. It is that simple. It really does not matter whether you fatigue the muscle in one set or several sets — as long as the muscle experiences a certain level of fatigue. In fact, this is supported by numerous research studies that have shown there are no significant differences when doing either one, two or three sets of an exercise . . . provided, of course, that the muscle was sufficiently fatigued. When performing multiple sets (i.e., more than one), muscular fatigue can be created by the cumulative effect of each successive set; with a single-set-to-failure (i.e., a quality set), muscular fatigue can be created by the cumulative effect of each successive repetition.

The following is a brief overview for administering a quality strength-training program:

THE QUALITY REPETITION

A quality program begins with a quality repetition. Indeed, the repetition is the most basic and integral aspect of a strength program. A repetition consists of raising the weight to the midrange position and lowering the weight to the starting/stretched position. (Raising a weight is typically referred to as the "positive phase" of a movement and involves a concentric muscular contraction; lowering a weight is also known as the "negative phase" of a movement and involves an eccentric muscular contraction.)

But what exactly is a quality repetition? Well, a quality repetition is performed by raising the weight in a deliberate, controlled manner in about 1-2 seconds. Lifting a weight in a rapid, explosive fashion is ill-advised for two reasons: (1) it exposes the muscles, joint structure and connective tissue to potentially dangerous forces which magnify the likelihood of an injury and (2) it increases the involvement of momentum which makes the exercise less productive and less efficient. In a quality repetition, the weight is lowered under control to the starting/ stretched position in about 3-4 seconds. The lowering of the weight should be emphasized because it makes the exercise more efficient: The same muscles that are used to raise the weight concentrically are also used to lower it eccentrically. Furthermore, lowering the weight in a controlled manner ensures that the exercised muscle is being stretched properly and safely. Finally, a quality repetition is done throughout the greatest possible range of motion (ROM) that safety allows — from a position of full stretch to a position of full muscular contraction and back to a position of full stretch. In general, a muscle must be exercised over a full ROM in order to receive a full-range effect. When exercising throughout a limited or partial ROM, only a portion of the muscle is fatigued thereby making the movement less efficient. Exercising throughout a full ROM is also necessary so that the flexibility of the joint is not compromised.

THE QUALITY SET

A series of quality repetitions is a quality set. A quality set is one that involves a relatively high level of intensity (or effort). This level of intensity is best achieved when training to the point of concentric muscular fatigue: when the muscles are exhausted to the extent that the weight cannot be raised for any additional repetitions. What happens during concentric muscular fatigue and why is it so effective and efficient? Let's say that the task is to perform a set of leg extensions with 100 pounds. In order to overcome inertia and provide impetus to the 100 pounds of resistance, the quadriceps must exert slightly more than 100 pounds of force. The weight will not move if a force less than or equal to 100 pounds is applied. During the first repetition, only a small percentage of the available muscle fibers is being worked — just enough to move the weight. As each repetition is performed, some muscle fibers will fatigue and will no longer be able to keep up with the increasing metabolic demands. Fresh fibers are simultaneously recruited to assist the fatigued fibers in generating ample force. This continues until the last repetition, when concentric muscular fatigue is finally reached. At this point, the available muscle fibers cannot collectively produce enough force to raise the weight. During this final repetition, the cumulative effect of each preceding repetition has fatigued the muscle thereby providing a very sufficient and efficient stimulus for muscular growth.

It should be noted that attempting a one-repetition maximum or performing low-repetition movements — that is, less than about three repetitions — significantly increases the risk of an injury. In general, concentric muscular fatigue should occur in 15-20 repetitions when exercising the hips, 10-15 repetitions for the legs and 6-12 repetitions for the upper torso.

THE QUALITY WORKOUT

A group of 17-19 quality sets comprises a quality workout. A quality workout emphasizes the major muscle groups — the hips, legs and upper torso — because those are the areas that are most frequently injured in sports. Moreover, a quality workout exercises the muscles from largest to smallest: the hips, legs (hamstrings, quadriceps, calves/dorsi flexors), upper torso (chest, upper back, shoulders), arms (biceps, triceps, forearms), abdominals and lower back. If an athlete is involved in a combative sport — such as wrestling or football — a quality workout includes an additional 2-4 neck exercises to strengthen the cervical area against possible injury. If neck exercises are to be included, they should be done at the beginning of the workout. A quality workout is performed 2-3 times per week on nonconsecutive days to allow for adequate recovery. Finally, the transition/recovery time between exercises should be minimal so that the duration of a quality workout is less than one hour per session.

THE QUALITY PROGRAM

A quality program is composed of quality workouts. The trademarks of a quality program are being safe, productive, efficient, comprehensive and practical. A quality program encourages progression in the weight used and/or the repetitions performed from one workout to the next. Lastly, accurate records are kept as a way of monitoring performance and making each workout more meaningful.

Despite its support by science and research, many strength coaches are somewhat cynical of this type of program. Numerous coaches still cling to the traditional program of endless sets and marathon workouts with an almost religious fervor and often justify these methods by saying, "Well, you are Princeton. You have to run that kind of program because of the time involved with academics." Statements like this miss the point entirely. Many schools — including Princeton University — have a rich and proud tradition of both academics and athletics. These schools place a high priority on academics yet they are still quite competitive in numerous sports on a national level. At any rate, shouldn't every school be concerned with making all aspects of their athletic programs more time-efficient? Come on, coaches, let's put the word "student" back in front of the word "athlete" where it belongs. Incidentally, the quality strength program that was described earlier is very similar to that currently used by many collegiate and professional teams. Indeed, a quality, time-efficient workout can be performed without sacrificing results.

REFERENCES

Bollig, L. E., ed. 1991. *1991-92 NCAA manual*. Overland Park, Kansas: The National Collegiate Athletic Association.

Brzycki, M. 1991. *A Practical Approach to Strength Training. 2nd ed*. Indianapolis, IN: Masters Press.

Chapter 4
DESIGNING A STRENGTH PROGRAM

Without a doubt, the most frequent mail I receive is from coaches who ask me to send them a copy of our strength program and/or to prescribe a routine based upon their available equipment.

This is the most difficult type of letter to answer directly. I usually send the coaches a copy of our strength-training manual along with some previously published material that is specific to their concerns. I will also suggest a strength-training routine that incorporates their existing equipment.

PROGRAM DESIGN

The reason why I cannot send an exact copy of our routine is because our workouts can vary considerably from one athlete to another. Our strength program is quite flexible and can take countless forms. We prescribe general guidelines for our athletes and allow them to choose whatever exercise they desire. For example, our athletes are required to perform one exercise for some muscle groups (hips, hamstrings, quadriceps, calves/dorsi flexors, biceps, triceps, abdominals and lower back) and two exercises for other muscle groups (chest, upper back and shoulders). In addition, our wrestlers perform 2-4 neck exercises and one lower-arm exercise (for the forearms). So a wrestler's routine consists of about 17-19 movements. They have the liberty to do any exercises they prefer and may use any equipment they desire. However, they are not permitted to perform any exercises that are potentially dangerous — such as barbell squats, power cleans, snatches and so on — or any other movements that may be contraindicated due to a previous injury or structural limitation.

Our program design for wrestling is summarized in Figure 1. Please note that the number in parentheses reflects the suggested movements for each particular body part.

EXERCISE CHOICES

I suspect that most high school weight rooms are equipped with a Universal Multi-Gym along with some free weights (that is, barbells and dumbbells) — although I have seen several high schools that have more equipment than some colleges and commercial gyms! In addition, you can always count on manual-resistance exercises as options. Figure 2 lists as many safe exercise choices as possible based upon the availability of these types of equipment. This will assist you and your athletes in designing routines. Lastly, a sample workout is listed in Figure 3.

SUMMING IT UP

As you can see, a strength-training routine can take almost an infinite number of forms. The only limits are your available equipment and your imagination. Give your athletes some general guidelines and then allow them to structure their own strength programs. In this way, they'll be less dependent on you and will be able to design a routine any time that you are unavailable such as during the summer, vacations and other absences. This will also make your athletes much more enthusiastic about strength training since it becomes less regimented.

Hopefully, this material has provided you with plenty of pertinent information. Best wishes for an injury-free year and a productive season!

FIGURE 1: Program Design for Wrestling		
1. Neck (2–4)	6.	Upper Arms
2. Hips (1)		a. Biceps (1)
3. Upper Legs		b. Triceps (1)
a. Hamstrings (1)	7.	Lower Arms (1)
b. Quadriceps (1)	8.	Abdominals (1)
4. Lower Legs	9.	Lower Back (1)
a. Calves or Dorsi Flexors (1)		
5. Upper Torso		
a. Chest (2)		
b. Upper Back (2)		
c. Shoulders (2)		

BODY PART	SELECTIONS	POSSIBLE EXERCISES	EQUIPMENT
		FIGURE 2: Exercise Choices for Barbells (B), Bodyweight (BW), Dumbbells (D), Manual Resistance (M) and Universal Multi-Gym (U)	
Neck	2–4	Neck Extension Neck Flexion Neck Lateral Flexion (L/R)	M M M
Hips	1	Leg Press Hip Abduction Hip Adduction	U M M
Hamstrings	1	Leg Curl	M,U
Quadriceps	1	Leg Extension	M,U
Lower Leg	1	Calf Raise Dorsi Flexion	BW,D,U M
Chest	2	Bench Press Bent-Arm Fly Decline Press Dip Incline Press Push-Up	B,D,U D,M B,D BW B,D BW,M
Upper Back	2	Bent-Over Row Chin Overhand Lat Pulldown Pullover Seated Row Underhand Lat Pulldown	B,D,M BW U B,D,M M,U U
Shoulders	2	Bent-Over Raise External Rotation Front Raise Internal Rotation Lateral Raise Seated Press Shoulder Shrug Upright Row	D,M D,M D,M D,M D,M B,D,M,U B,D,U B,D,M,U
Biceps	1	Bicep Curl	B,D,M,U
Triceps	1	Tricep Extension	B,D,M,U
Lower Arms	1	Wrist Extension Wrest Flexion	D,M,U B,D,M,U
Abdominals	1	Knee-Up Side Bend Sit-Up	BW,M D,U BW,M
Lower Back	1	Back Extension	BW,M

FIGURE 3: Sample Routine	
Neck Flexion (M)	
Neck Extension (M)	
Leg Press (U)	
Leg Curl (M)	
Leg Extension (U)	
Calf Raise (U)	
Bench Press (B)	
Bent-Arm Fly (M)	
Chin (BW)	
Pullover (D)	
Lateral Raise (M)	
Shoulder Shrug (B)	
Bicep Curl (U)	
Tricep Extension (M)	**Equipment Codes:**
Wrist Flexion (B)	**Barbell (B),**
	Bodyweight (BW),
	Dumbbell (D),
Sit-Up (M)	**Manual Resistance (M),**
Back Extension (BW)	**Universal Multi-Gym (U)**

Chapter 5
STIMULATING MUSCULAR GROWTH

Wrestlers who wish to move up to a higher weight class must increase their muscle mass. What is needed to produce muscular growth? Surprisingly, it is very little.

THE THREE REQUIREMENTS

Three requirements are necessary for muscular growth to occur. If these three conditions are met, a muscle will respond by increasing in both size and strength. The degree to which a given muscle will grow then becomes a function of an individual's genetic profile, most notably the insertion points of tendons, limb lengths, predominant fiber types and neurological efficiency. Incidentally, genetics are the primary reason why two individuals can have a different response to training despite using the same strength program.

The three requirements that must occur are progressive overload, adequate recovery and proper nourishment.

Progressive Overload

The first requirement is that a stress or a load must be applied to a muscle using some form of resistance. Your muscles do not have eyes and, therefore, do not know what your muscles are lifting. In other words, it does not matter whether the resistance is being supplied by a barbell, a machine, a partner or even a cinder block.

What matters, however, is that the load must be great enough to provide a sufficient stimulus for growth to take place. Failure to "overload" a muscle with sufficient stress will result in submaximal gains. Unfortunately, no one knows exactly how much stress is necessary to stimulate growth. The only way to ensure that a muscle received enough stress is by training with maximal intensity (or effort). The following example should make things more clear:

Did you ever have a coach who asked you to wrestle with somewhat less than maximal effort? Well, it is impossible to measure any specific level of effort that is productive . . . except for maximal effort. Let's try to draw a parallel between this situation and strength training. Suppose that 85% intensity created adequate stress for a muscle to get stronger. How do you know if you are training with a level of intensity that is 85% . . . or 90% . . . or any other level? The fact is that the only desirable level of intensity that you can measure accurately is 100% or an all-out effort. (A level of intensity should not be confused with a percentage of maximal weight.) Therefore, the only way to ensure that your muscles have received an overload is by training with maximal intensity. This is typified by lifting to the point of momentary muscular fatigue — that is, when no further repetitions are possible.

Lastly, the overload must be progressive. Every workout, your athletes should attempt to perform one more repetition that the last time, use more resistance than the previous session or both.

Adequate Recovery

A second requirement is that your muscles must be allowed to recover from strength workouts. It is during the recovery period that a muscle adapts to the imposed stress. If a strength-training program does not provide for adequate recovery, your wrestlers will gradually reach an overtrained state with a resulting loss in muscular size and strength.

Some individuals have a high tolerance for exercise and recover quickly; others have a low tolerance for exercise and recover slowly. You can determine if any of your wrestlers have a low tolerance for exercise by monitoring their progress in the weight room. These individuals will need a little more recovery time.

Generally speaking, most individuals require about 48-72 hours of recovery time between strength workouts. This means that your wrestlers should strength train three times per week (every other day). Their increased activity level from practices will necessitate more recovery time. So during the season, you will need to reduce their sessions in the weight room to twice a week. One workout should come the day after your meet and the next session should be done no sooner than 48 hours before your next meet.

Proper Nourishment

The last requirement is that the body receives proper nourishment as a fuel for growth. Remember, you can have a car with the most finely tuned, powerful engine in the world but it won't respond properly with lousy gasoline.

SUMMING IT UP

It should be evident that the strength training of your athletes does not have to be complicated. Your wrestlers need to train each set with maximal effort, allow themselves an adequate recovery period and eat properly. In short, for a muscle to get stronger, you must stress it, rest it and feed it. The result will speak for itself.

Chapter 6

FIBER TYPES AND REPETITION RANGES

Your genetic makeup is the single most important ingredient in determining your response from strength training. One of the most influential of all your inherited characteristics is the distribution and composition of your muscle fibers.

Your muscle fiber type plays a major role in dictating your potential for improving your muscular size and physical strength. You can maximize your response to strength training by using repetition ranges that are most suited to your muscle fiber type.

MUSCLE FIBER TYPES

Fiber types may be grouped into two major categories: slow twitch (ST) or Type I and fast twitch (FT) or Type II. These two major fiber types differ in several areas including speed of contraction, force of contraction and endurance capacity. FT fibers can contract quickly and generate large amounts of force, but they fatigue rather easily. Relative to FT muscle fibers, ST fibers contract slower and produce less force, but they have greater endurance. (Some researchers also recognize one or more intermediate fiber types that possess characteristics of both FT and ST fibers.)

Your muscles are composed of both fiber types and the different types are intermingled throughout each muscle. However, the distribution of FT and ST fibers within each muscle is genetically determined. In fact, studies of twins indicate that muscle-fiber composition is determined almost entirely by hereditary factors. Some athletes have inherited a predominant fiber type that allows them to be successful during efforts of varying durations. For example, a wrestler who has inherited a high percentage of FT fibers has the genetic potential to generate tremendous amounts of force in a rather short period of time and, therefore, will excel during short-term, high-intensity efforts; on the other hand, a wrestler who has inherited a high percentage of ST fibers has the genetic potential to display large amounts of muscular endurance and, therefore, will excel during long-term, low-intensity efforts. It should also be noted that your fiber-type mixture will likely differ from one muscle to another and may even vary from one side of your body to the other.

IMPLICATIONS

The technical term for an increase in muscular size is "hypertrophy." (Its inverse — a decrease in muscular size — is called "atrophy.") Both FT and ST muscle fibers have the potential for hypertrophy. However, FT fibers display a much greater capacity for hypertrophy than ST fibers. In other words, wrestlers who have inherited a high percentage of FT fibers will have a greater potential to increase the size of their muscles. Because FT fibers can produce greater force than ST fibers, these wrestlers will also exhibit a higher potential for improvements in muscular strength.

Your potential for muscular endurance is also based upon your inherited fiber-type mixture. For example, if you have a high percentage of ST fibers, you will have greater muscular endurance than someone who has a high percentage of FT fibers. Researchers tested an individual who could only perform one repetition with 80% of his maximal strength. Another person was able to execute 34 repetitions with 83% of her maximal strength before reaching muscular fatigue. She had an identical twin sister who also performed 34 repetitions with 83% of her maximal strength. Interestingly, neither woman was present while the other was being tested, and neither knew the results until after both had been tested.

Incidentally, there's no definitive proof that strength training increases the number of muscle fibers in humans. An increase in the number of muscle fibers — known as "hyperplasia" — has been demonstrated in animals but not in humans. In addition, no conclusive evidence exists to suggest that strength training will change your ST fibers to FT fibers or vice versa. Though one type of muscle fiber may take on certain metabolic characteristics of the other type of fiber, actual conversion appears to be impossible. In other words, you cannot convert one fiber type into another any more than you can make a racehorse out of a mule. So if you took a mule and trained it like a racehorse, you might get a faster mule . . . but you will never get a racehorse.

WHAT'S YOUR TYPE?

The only way to positively determine your fiber-type distribution is by removing a small section of your muscle by way of a biopsy and analyzing the tissue sample under a microscope. Needless to say, most people are reluctant to part with samples of their muscle tissue.

One way of guesstimating muscle-fiber type in a far less painful way is by testing muscular endurance. This is a crude but reasonably effective way of assessing muscle-fiber types based upon fatigue characteristics. Because a muscular endurance test involves determining a one-repetition maximum (1-RM), this test is not recommended for use with conventional equipment. Nevertheless, endurance testing is still quite interesting and deserves special note. Suppose your 1-RM in the leg extension is 200 pounds. An endurance test is performed with 80% of maximal strength or, in this case, 160 pounds. If you can do a relatively high number of repetitions with 160 pounds (more than about 15), you can assume that your quadriceps are composed primarily of ST fibers; if you perform a rather low number of repetitions with 160 pounds (less than about 5), it is likely that your quadriceps have a high percentage of FT fibers. Because the distribution of fiber types varies from muscle to muscle, an endurance test would have to be performed for each muscle group. Again, this test is not recommended for use with conventional equipment because it involves obtaining a potentially dangerous 1-RM.

You can also make a logical guesstimate of your fiber-type makeup based upon performance variables. If you excel in efforts that require muscular endurance, you have probably inherited a high percentage of ST muscle fibers; similarly, if you excel in efforts that require speed, strength and/or power, you have likely inherited a high percentage of FT muscle fibers.

Another way of making a reasonable assessment of your muscle-fiber type is by evaluating your muscular development. Remember, FT fibers have a much greater capacity for hypertrophy than ST fibers. Therefore, if you have well-developed muscles you probably have a high percentage of FT fibers; conversely, if you have slight muscular development you probably have a high percentage of ST fibers.

REPETITION RANGES

Once you have a general idea of your fiber type, you can use this to customize your repetition ranges thereby maximizing your response to strength training. Your muscles must be exercised for a certain amount of time with an appropriate level of intensity in order for them to increase in size and strength. In general, optimal time frames are about 90-120 seconds for your hips, 60-90 seconds for your legs and 40-70 seconds for your upper torso. (The muscles of your lower body should be exercised for a slightly longer duration because of their greater size and work capacity.)

It is not usually practical for you to perform a set for a precise amount of time. However, you can use these optimal time frames to formulate repetition ranges. For instance, if you raise a weight in about two seconds and lower it in about four seconds, each repetition would be approximately six seconds long. Dividing six seconds into the time frames that were previously noted yields the following repetition ranges: 15-20 for your hips, 10-15 for your legs and about 6-12 for your upper body. Remember, these repetition ranges are based upon a six-second repetition. If you did negative-only repetitions that were eight seconds long, the time frames mentioned earlier would be divided by 8 seconds and result in the following repetition ranges: 11-15 for your hips, 8-11 for your legs and 5-8 for your upper torso.

So repetition ranges are not as important as the length of time that a muscle is exercised. However, it is usually much more practical to count repetitions during a workout than to be followed around by someone with a stopwatch. It should be noted that attempting a 1-RM or performing low-repetition movements that are considerably less than those dictated by the optimal time frames increases your risk of injury. Likewise, as an exercise exceeds the recommended time frames, it becomes a greater test of your aerobic endurance rather than your muscular strength.

Some wrestlers — because of a predominant muscle-fiber type — may require slightly higher or slightly lower repetition ranges than previously suggested in order to maximize their response to strength training. For example, wrestlers who have inherited a high percentage of ST muscle fibers would probably benefit more from strength training by performing slightly higher repetitions because their high percentage of ST fibers are more suited for muscular endurance. Slightly higher ranges of perhaps 20-25 for the hips, 15-20 for the legs and 10-15 for the upper body would probably produce a better response for someone with a predominance of ST fibers in those body parts. Conversely, wrestlers who have inherited a high percentage of FT muscle fibers would probably benefit more from strength training by performing slightly lower repetitions because their high percentage of FT fibers limit their muscular endurance. Slightly lower repetition ranges of perhaps 10-15 for the hips, 9-12 for the legs and 6-8 for the upper body would probably produce a better response for someone with a predominance of FT fibers in those body parts. In a 1987 study, sprinters trained with low repetitions, middle-distance runners with medium repetitions and long-distance runners with high repetitions. The study revealed excellent and equal strength gains in all three groups. (Successful sprinters likely inherit a high percentage of FT fibers and successful distance runners likely inherit a high percentage of ST fibers.)

One final point about FT and ST fibers: The use of lower repetitions is not recommended to convert ST fibers to FT fibers. Likewise, the use of higher repetitions is not suggested to convert FT fibers to ST fibers. Performing higher or lower repetition ranges is done to maximize your response based upon your already-established predominant muscle-fiber type.

Chapter 7
VARY YOUR WORKOUTS

The stimulus for muscular growth can be produced quite effectively by a system based upon brief exercise of high intensity that incorporates a progressive overload. This means that an athlete should attempt to perform one more repetition than last time and/or use more resistance than during the previous sessions. Assuming adequate recovery and proper nourishment, one set of each prescribed exercise performed to the point of momentary muscular fatigue — that is, when no further repetitions are possible — will promote maximal possible gains in both size and strength.

THE STRENGTH "PLATEAU"

Sooner or later, athletes will reach a point in the course of their training where strength gains have leveled off or reached a "plateau." Quite often, this is a result of overtraining — the athletes are performing entirely too much work causing their muscular systems to be overstressed. In effect, the demands have exceeded their recovery ability. In this case, the athletes need to reduce the volume of work being done in the weight room.

Sometimes, however, strength will plateau due to performing the same routine each session over long periods of time. The workout becomes a form of unproductive manual labor that is monotonous and dull.

How can a coach prevent this situation from occurring? Quite simply, the answer is to vary the stimulus. A number of ways exist in which a routine may be modified. In some cases, only one or two parts of the workout need to be changed.

Rearrange the Order

One of the easiest ways to modify a workout is to rearrange the order in which the exercises for a particular body part are performed. Suppose an athlete's shoulder strength reaches a plateau. If the original prescription called for an upright row followed by a seated press, the athlete can switch these two movements, performing the seated press first and the upright row next.

Remember, when varying the order of exercises, the weights must be adjusted accordingly. Let's say an athlete uses 90 pounds in the upright row followed immediately by a seated press using 100 pounds. If the order is changed — that is, the seated press is done first — the athlete's shoulder musculature will be relatively fresh for the seated press and, therefore, more resistance could be handled. However, less weight must be used in the upright row since the shoulders will be more fatigued than usual.

An additional possibility is to exercise the muscle groups in a different sequence. Instead of going from chest to upper back to shoulders, an athlete might do shoulders, chest then upper back. Again, the weights must be adjusted accordingly.

Change the Modality

Another way to vary an athlete's training is to change the modality or equipment used. If an athlete reaches a plateau on the bench press and desires a change, the same movement can be performed using different equipment. A bench press may be done with a barbell, dumbbells, manual resistance or any of the various bench-press machines (selectorized or plate-loaded) available on the market. Remember, your muscles do not have eyes and, therefore, are unable to distinguish how the resistance is being applied. Obviously, the extent to which this variation can be accomplished depends upon the equipment on hand.

Alternate the Exercises

A third means of varying the stimulus is to alternate the exercises that involve the same muscle group(s). For instance, a bench press, incline press, decline press, dip and manual-resistance push-up all work the chest, shoulders and triceps. As such, when an athlete peaks in one of the exercises, another movement can be substituted that employs the same musculature. Once again, the availability of equipment will determine how much the exercises may be alternated.

Vary the Style

A final option is to vary the style in which a particular exercise is performed. The leg extension, for example, may be done at least four different ways. The typical way is to do the exercise using both legs at the same time (bilaterally). In addition, the movement may be done using one leg at a time (unilaterally). The leg extension may also be performed in a "negative-only" manner by having a training partner raise the weight and allowing the lifter to lower the weight under control in about 6-8 seconds per repetition. A fourth way is to do the exercise in a "negative-accentuated" fashion in which the lifter raises the weight with both legs, lowers the weight with one leg, raises the weight with both legs and lowers the weight with the other leg.

SUMMING IT UP

Do not forget, only one set of each prescribed exercise done to the point of muscular fatigue is necessary to stimulate maximal gains. No more than about 17-19 exercises should be performed during any one workout. The routine should take about 60 minutes or less to complete. When coupled with adequate recover (about 48-72 hours between workouts) and proper nourishment, this stimulus will be enough to promote the greatest possible gains within an individual's genetically imposed limitations. Keep in mind that doing any more than the suggested amount of exercises may produce overtraining which will adversely affect the potential results.

Occasionally, the workouts of your athletes need to be changed. At least four ways exist to modify workouts: (1) rearrange the order of exercises; (2) change the modality/equipment; (3) alternate the exercises that involve the same muscle group(s); and (4) vary the style in which an exercise is performed. By providing for variety in training, coaches will enhance their athletes' compliance to the strength programs and ensure that their strength gains continue.

Chapter 8
METABOLIC CONDITIONING
— PART I

Most wrestlers typically perform their strength training separate from their conditioning activities. On the mat, however, wrestlers are required to integrate their muscular strength with their aerobic conditioning.

Metabolic conditioning is essentially a combination of intense strength training (or other anaerobic efforts) and aerobic conditioning. It involves three major biological systems: the musculoskeletal, respiratory and circulatory systems. In order for you to improve your metabolic coditioning, these three systems must share the physiological demands.

Unfortunately, conditioning of the metabolic system is rarely emphasized or even addressed. However, a thorough understanding of metabolic conditioning and an application of specific training techniques can enhance your functional fitness.

PROJECT TOTAL CONDITIONING

In the early 1970s, research designated as "Project Total Conditioning" was conducted at the United States Military Academy in New York. The research used members of several athletic teams at the academy as test subjects. Project Total Conditioning actually consisted of a number of different studies. However, the main portion of Project Total Conditioning was a six-week study that examined metabolic conditioning. An experimental group consisted of 18 varsity football players from the academy. (A 19th subject was injured during spring football practice.) This group performed a strength-training workout three times per week on alternate days with two days rest after the third workout of the week. Each workout consisted of ten exercises and took an average of about 30 minutes to complete. (The subjects also performed six neck exercises twice per week.) Each subject was required to perform as many repetitions as possible using proper technique in every exercise of every workout. One set of each exercise was done to the point of muscular fatigue within a repetition range of 5-12. The group took a minimal amount of recovery time between exercises.

In order to minimize the influence of the so-called "learning effect," the experimental group followed the training protocol for two weeks prior to the study. (The learning effect refers to the often dramatic increases initially attained by individuals which is attributable to improvement in their neurological functioning not muscular strength.) Prior to the six-week study, the subjects were pretested in several areas — including body composition, strength, cardiovascular fitness, the 40-yard dash, the vertical jump and flexibility — and were retested following the study.

The study produced very compelling results. After six weeks of training, the subjects increased the resistance they used between their first and seventeenth workouts by an average of 58.54%. The minimum improvement in strength was 45.61% while the maximal increase in strength was 69.70%. (Incidentally, the average increase in the resistance that was used between their second and sixteenth workouts was 43.06%.) The subjects also increased the number of repetitions they performed between their first and seventeenth workouts by an average of 6.59%.

Interestingly, the time that the subjects needed to complete their workouts decreased substantially. Comparing the first workout to the seventeenth, the experimental group reduced the average duration of their workouts by 24.09% — from an average of 37.73 minutes to an average of 28.64 minutes. Two individuals almost literally cut their workout times in half — one from 49 to 25 minutes and the other from 43 to 22 minutes — yet increased their strength levels by 68.32% and 65.59%, respectively. A third individual reduced his workout time from 42 to 27 minutes and increased his strength by 66.32%.

Besides the tremendous improvements in muscular strength, the subjects also reduced their average time in the two-mile run by 88 seconds — from an average of 13:18 [13 minutes and 18 seconds] to an average of 11:50. This represented an average improvement of 11% — without having performed any running except during the course of spring football practice (which occurred during the first four weeks of training). The subjects also had lower resting heart rates following the six weeks of training. In addition, the experimental group had lower exercising heart rates at various workloads on a stationary cycle and they were able to perform more work before reaching heart rates of 170 beats per minute.

At the end of the six-week study, the experimental group had reduced their average time in the 40-yard dash from 5.1467 seconds to 5.0933 seconds — a 1.04% improvement. Their vertical jump had increased from an average of 22.6 inches to an average of 24.067 inches — an average improvement of 6.49%. Finally, their average improvement in three flexibility measures was 10.92%.

These striking results are even more impressive when you consider that they were accomplished in such a time-efficient manner. In fact, the total amount of actual training time performed by each individual during the six-week program averaged *less than 8.5 hours* — which is *less than 30 minutes per workout*. It should be noted that the test subjects were highly conditioned football players who were already quite strong and fit at the start of the program. Nevertheless, the study demonstrated the effects of short-duration, high-intensity strength training on metabolic conditioning.

Chapter 9
METABOLIC CONDITIONING
— PART II

IMPROVING METABOLIC CONDITIONING

You can improve your metabolic conditioning by simply performing your strength training with a high level of intensity while taking very little rest between exercises. Performed in this fashion, the shared demands placed on your major biological systems create a metabolic conditioning effect that cannot be approached by traditional methods of training. The two most popular types of metabolic workouts are high-intensity training and circuit training.

HIGH-INTENSITY TRAINING (HIT)

One form of metabolic conditioning that has recently seen a renewed interest is high-intensity training or, simply, HIT. In the early 1970s, Nautilus inventor Arthur Jones popularized the brief, intense strength-training workouts that would later become known as "HIT" in the mid-1980s. In recent years, HIT has gradually become increasingly popular among highly competitive male and female athletes in a variety of sports and activities. HIT is currently used by professional athletes in the National Basketball Association, the National Hockey League and Major League Baseball as well as roughly one dozen teams in the National Football League. In addition, HIT is used by thousands of collegiate athletes who participate in virtually every sport imaginable — and the numbers are growing.

There are many interpretations and variations of HIT. However, most versions of HIT have several common denominators. As the name implies, HIT is characterized by intense, aggressive efforts — each exercise is typically performed to the point of muscular fatigue or "failure." A minimal number of sets is usually performed

— often only one set of each exercise but sometimes as many as three sets. Another characteristic of HIT is the emphasis on progressive overload — whenever possible, an attempt is made to increase the repetitions that are performed and/or the resistance that is used from one workout to the next. With safety as a major concern, HIT does not include explosive movements or excessive momentum — all repetitions are done with a controlled speed of movement. Additionally, HIT is comprehensive — training all of the major muscle groups is a priority.

In general, HIT also involves very brief workouts with a minimum amount of recovery taken between exercises. The short recovery interval between exercises enables you to maintain a fairly high heart rate for the duration of the workout. Like other forms of metabolic conditioning, the length of the recovery interval taken between exercises depends upon your present level of metabolic fitness. The recovery period is not structured, timed or predetermined. Initially, however, a recovery time of perhaps three minutes may be necessary between efforts; with improved fitness, your pace should be quickened to the point where you are moving as rapidly as possible between exercises.

In short, HIT places an incredible workload upon every major muscle in your body and, at the same time, stresses your circulatory and respiratory pathways. Furthermore, this type of workout can be used to improve your metabolic conditioning in a safe and time-efficient manner.

CIRCUIT TRAINING

One of the oldest and most popular forms of metabolic conditioning has been dubbed "circuit training." The birth of circuit training can be traced back to England in the 1950s. With circuit training, the idea is to perform a series of exercises (or activities) in a sequence or "circuit" with a very brief recovery period between each "station." In a sense, therefore, circuit training is a form of interval training.

Circuit Weight Training

The merger of circuit training with weight training is known as "circuit weight training" or, simply, CWT. Usually, CWT is performed on a multi-station apparatus — such as a Universal Multi-Gym. There are several advantages in using multi-station equipment for CWT. First of all, the exercises of multi-station equipment are in close proximity to each other and that allows you to move quickly around the circuit. Secondly, the selectorized weight stacks of multi-station equipment enable you to make faster and easier adjustments in resistance. Nevertheless, CWT can also be performed with single-station pieces and/or free weights provided that the distance between the equipment is not too great.

CWT is very versatile — the number of exercises/stations, the number of repetitions performed and the amount of recovery taken between movements can be manipulated. The number of exercises done in the circuit and the amount of recovery taken between the exercises is a function of your level of fitness. However, a comprehensive session of CWT involves a series of about 12-14 exercises or stations that target each of your major muscle groups. A total-body circuit on a Universal Multi-Gym might as follows: leg press, leg curl, leg extension, bench press, dip, pull-up, lat pulldown, seated press, shoulder shrug, bicep curl, tricep extension, wrist flexion and sit-up. (Several other productive exercises can be done on most multi-station equipment including the upright row, knee-up and side bend.)

At each station, you can either perform a given number of repetitions or do as many repetitions as possible during a specified time frame (with a controlled speed of movement). At a pace of 60 seconds per exercise with 30 seconds of recovery between stations (including the set-up for the next exercise), you can complete a circuit of 12-14 stations in as little as 18-21 minutes. It should be noted that the resistance used at each station should permit you to reach muscular fatigue by the end of the allotted exercise time.

To ensure that you obtain continued metabolic improvements from CWT, your metabolic system can be progressively overloaded by (1) increasing the resistance used at a given station; (2) increasing the length of the work interval (thereby doing more repetitions); (3) decreasing the length of the recovery interval taken between stations; or (4) any combination of the three previous options.

To summarize CWT: You begin at a particular station and complete one set of an exercise. After this, you move to the next station in the circuit, prepare for the next exercise and rest for the remainder of the recovery period. This cycle is repeated over and over again until you complete the entire circuit.

Circuit Aerobic Training

In the last few years, there's been a growing interest in circuit aerobic training (CAT) which involves a series of aerobic activities or stations. The circuit can be designed a number of different ways — the number of aerobic activities, the duration and intensity of each activity and the amount of recovery taken between stations can be varied. Most of these variables are dependent upon your fitness level. Your goal, however, is to perform the equivalent of about 20-60 minutes of aerobic exercise with an appropriate level of effort. Keep in mind that 30 minutes of exercise can be done as one 30-minute session, two 15-minute sessions, three 10-minute sessions or even six 5-minute sessions. So you might exercise for 10 minutes on a stationary cycle, 10 minutes on a rower and 10 minutes on a stair-climbing machine for a total of 30 minutes of aerobic activity. Or you might perform each of those same three activities for five minutes but repeat the circuit twice for a total of 30 minutes. Regardless, your level of intensity should be as high as possible during the efforts. (It probably would not be practical — or permissible — for you to monopolize a group of activities for intervals of less than five minutes per station in a commercial facility.)

Other Variations

Yet another version of circuit training is to integrate weight-training exercises with one or more aerobic-training activities. For instance, you might do a strength-training exercise, pedal a stationary cycle for 1-3 minutes, do another strength-training exercise, pedal a stationary cycle for another 1-3 minutes and so on.

The "Fitness Trail" is a form of circuit training that originated in several of the Scandinavian countries. This method of circuit training is performed outdoors in a natural environment such as a park. A typical Fitness Trail consists of numerous stations that are positioned several hundred yards apart and arranged along a circuitous route. A wrestler would run to a station, stop and perform some type of agility (i.e., hurdles, log walks and vaults), calisthenic (i.e., push-ups, sit-ups, chins and dips) or flexibility exercise and then proceed to the next station.

THE METABOLIC CHALLENGE

Metabolic conditioning presents an enormous physiological challenge to your musculoskeletal, respiratory and circulatory systems. By combining strength training with aerobic activities, you can improve your metabolic fitness and better prepare yourself for wrestling — a sport in which you are required to integrate your muscular strength with your aerobic conditioning.

Chapter 10

THE PRE-EXHAUSTION PRINCIPLE: BYPASSING THE WEAK LINK

Essentially, there are two types of exercise movements: single joint and multiple joint. A single-joint movement — also known as a "simple" or "primary" movement — involves a range of motion around only one joint. The advantage of a single-joint movement is that it usually isolates a muscle. A good example is a leg extension in which the lower leg rotates around the knee joint thereby isolating the quadriceps muscle located on the front thigh.

On the other hand, a multiple-joint movement — also known as a "compound" or "secondary" movement — involves ranges of motion around more than one joint. For instance, during a lat pulldown, there is rotation around both the shoulder and the elbow joints — the upper back (or "lats") rotates the upper arm around the shoulder joint and the biceps bend the arm at the elbow joint. The forearm flexors are also used to maintain a grip on the bar. Multiple-joint exercises are advantageous because a relatively large amount of muscle mass can be used in one movement.

THE WEAK LINK

There's an old saying that a chain is only as strong as its weakest link. That adage also applies to multiple-joint movements. Indeed, multiple-joint movements have a distinct disadvantage because they generally have a "weak link." When you fatigue in an exercise it is because your smaller and weaker muscles become exhausted. This happens well before your larger and stronger muscles have received a sufficient workload. In an exercise like a lat pulldown, your biceps are the smaller muscle and, therefore, will fatigue long before your upper back. In fact, your grip strength may be the first to exhaust. Whenever a multiple-joint movement is performed for the upper back — such as a lat pulldown or a seated row — the lifter will quickly notice that the biceps and forearms received much more work than the upper back. So the biceps and forearms get a pretty good workout but the upper back — which the athlete is really trying to exercise — gets very little workload.

As a rule of thumb, the arms are the weak link when performing multiple-joint movements for the upper body. Likewise, the legs are the weak link when performing multiple-joint movements for the hips. Because of the existence of these weak links in multiple-joint movements, the potential for athletes to develop their larger, more powerful muscle structures is limited. The question is: How can you avoid this problem?

PRE-EXHAUSTION

The problem associated with multiple-joint movements can be avoided by utilizing the Pre-Exhaustion Principle — a training technique that was first popularized in the early 1970s. The Pre-Exhaustion Principle employs what has been called a "double set": one single-joint movement followed quickly by a multiple-joint movement. With the Pre-Exhaustion Principle, the idea is to "pre-exhaust" the muscles you are trying to work by first performing a single-joint exercise. In effect, this will bypass the weak link. The first exercise is followed quickly by a second exercise to bring into play other surrounding muscles that provide assistance to work the pre-fatigued muscle to a point beyond its normal state of exhaustion. For instance, let's suppose that you want to exercise your upper back using the Pre-Exhaustion Principle. First, you would perform a single-joint exercise — such as a barbell, dumbbell or machine pullover — to pre-fatigue your upper back. As soon as possible following the completion of that exercise, you would perform a multiple-joint movement — such as a lat pulldown, seated row or chin. That second set will employ your arms to assist your pre-fatigued upper back to work to a degree of exhaustion that would normally be impossible.

It should be noted that for maximal results, the second exercise should come as soon as possible following the completion of the first exercise. Too much time between the first and second exercises will allow the pre-fatigued muscle to gradually recover some of its original level of strength. If the muscle recovers too much, then you are back to where you started with the weak link still being the limiting factor.

PRACTICAL APPLICATIONS

The following is a brief guide for devising "double sets" to pre-exhaust your major muscle groups:

Hips

Individuals fatigue in the leg press when they exhaust the strength of their quadriceps. So a leg press is a great exercise for developing your front thigh but it is a relatively poor exercise for developing your hips. However, your hips can be pre-fatigued first by performing a single-joint exercise — such as a hip extension or hip abduction (on a machine or with manual resistance). Then if this single-joint exercise is followed quickly by the leg press, your fresh quadriceps and hamstrings can be used to fatigue your hips to a greater degree than would otherwise be possible.

Hamstrings

The leg curl is the main single-joint exercise used to isolate the "hams" on the back of your thigh. Performing a leg press soon after completion of the leg curl uses your hips and quadriceps to allow you to further exhaust your hamstrings.

Quadriceps

The single-joint movement that is best for isolating your "quads" is the leg extension. Once again, the leg press can be used as a secondary movement. In this case, your hips and hamstrings are used to exercise your pre-fatigued quadriceps.

Chest

A single-joint movement that provides direct resistance to the pectoral muscles of your chest is the bent-arm fly using dumbbells or manual resistance. (Actually, this movement also works your anterior deltoid located on the front part of your shoulder.) After pre-fatiguing your chest region with the bent-arm fly, your "pecs" can be further exhausted by doing any one of a number of multiple-joint movements — depending, of course, upon the available equipment. Popular multiple-joint movements for your chest include the bench press, decline press, incline press, push-up and dip. Performing one of these multiple-joint movements soon after completion of the bent-arm fly uses your triceps to further exhaust your pectoral area. (It should be noted that for variety, the bent-arm fly can be performed in the decline, incline and supine positions.)

Upper Back

Your upper back can be effectively isolated with conventional equipment by using a barbell, dumbbell or machine pullover. Involving your fresh biceps during a multiple-joint movement like a chin, pull-up, seated row, bent-over row or lat pulldown immediately after the pullover will allow you to exercise your upper back in a highly efficient manner.

Shoulders

Your shoulder musculature includes the deltoids and the trapezius. The most popular single-joint movements for addressing the muscles of your deltoid using conventional equipment are the lateral raise (middle deltoid), front raise (anterior deltoid) and bent-over raise (posterior deltoid). A shoulder shrug is the best single-joint exercise for isolating your trapezius. A "double set" for your deltoids would include one of the three single-joint exercises for the deltoids followed quickly by a seated (or shoulder) press. The seated press uses your triceps to assist in exercising your pre-fatigued deltoids. A "double set" for your trapezius would be the shoulder shrug followed as soon as possible by an upright row. The upright row is a multiple-joint movement that uses your biceps to help pre-exhaust your trapezius.

Biceps

The bicep curl is the best single-joint exercise for isolating your biceps muscle. Located on the front part of your upper arm, your biceps are used to flex your lower arm around your elbow joint. Performing a multiple-joint movement like a chin, pull-up, seated row, bent-over row or lat pulldown soon after doing the bicep curl allows you to use your upper back to exhaust your biceps even further.

Triceps

Your triceps are found on the back of your upper arm and are used to extend your lower arm around your elbow joint. The single-joint movement that is best for exercising your triceps is the tricep extension — which can be done standing, sitting or lying. The bench press, decline press, incline press, dip or seated press can be used as a multiple-joint movement. In this manner, your chest and/or anterior deltoid are used to exercise your pre-fatigued triceps.

THE BOTTOM LINE

Remember, the limiting factor in multiple-joint movements is the smaller, weaker muscle structures. However, the disadvantage can be turned into an advantage by first pre-fatiguing your muscles with a single-joint movement and then immediately performing a multiple-joint movement to involve surrounding muscles for assistance. In this way, you will maximize your muscular development in a safe, efficient manner.

Chapter 11
GETTING THE MOST OUT
OF DIPS AND CHINS

Dips and chins are two excellent, basic movements that exercise every major muscle group in the upper torso. Dips challenge the chest (or "pecs"), the front portion of the shoulder and the triceps; chins provide work for the upper-back region (or "lats"), the biceps and much of the forearm musculature. In addition to affecting a rather large amount of muscle tissue, dips and chins are great exercises for wrestlers since they both involve movement of a person's entire body mass.

Dips and chins should both be performed for about 8-12 repetitions, with each repetition lasting about six seconds. Once wrestlers can do more than 12 repetitions in good form, they should add resistance to their bodyweight. This can be accomplished one of two ways. One way is to have a training partner place his hands on the lifter's waist and supply as much resistance as necessary. Unfortunately, there is no way of knowing exactly how much additional resistance is being applied. A better way is to have the lifters tie or secure weights around their waists. In this manner, the lifters will be able to systematically increase the resistance whenever they achieve the maximal number of repetitions.

EXERCISES

The following are descriptions for the proper performance of each exercise:

Dip

Grasp the handles and assume a stretched position with your knees bent and your ankles crossed. To do the exercise, raise your body to the mid-range position by extending your arms but not allowing your elbows to "lock." Pause briefly in this position and then return under control to the starting position to obtain a sufficient stretch.

To get the most out of this exercise, make sure that it is performed throughout a full range of motion (ROM) — from a position of full stretch (chest near the handles), to a position of muscular contraction (without "locking" your elbows) and then back to the stretched position.

Chin

Reach up, grasp the bar with your palms facing you and space your hands approximately shoulder-width apart. Bring your body to a "dead hang" and cross your ankles. To perform the exercise, pull yourself up to the mid-range position so that your upper chest touches the bar and your elbows rotate backward. Pause briefly in this position and then lower yourself under control back to the starting position to ensure a proper stretch.

For optimal results, try to touch your chest to the bar rather than your chin. This will increase the ROM of the exercise. Rotating your elbows backward in the mid-range of the movement will increase the workload performed by your upper back. Extend your arms fully at the end of each repetition to obtain an adequate stretch.

Chapter 12

MANUAL RESISTANCE
FOR WRESTLERS

Quite often, coaches find it difficult — if not impossible — to budget enough time for their wrestlers to strength train during the season. Sometimes, merely gaining access to the weight room is a problem.

Manual resistance (MR) is often referred to as a "productive alternative" for developing strength when equipment is not available or when time is limited. It is an extremely effective way of strength training in which a partner/spotter supplies the resistance. MR was refined and popularized during the late 1970s by Dan Riley when he was the strength coach at Penn State. [Editor's note: At the time of this publication, Dan was the strength coach of the Houston Texans of the National Football League.] A large number of collegiate and professional teams include MR exercises in the programs of their athletes.

GENERAL GUIDELINES

Instead of counting repetitions, it is suggested that each MR exercise be done for a specified length of time. Research indicates that the optimal time frame for strength training the upper-body musculature is between 40-70 seconds. An upper-body exercise performed for less than about 40 seconds has a higher risk of injury; likewise, an exercise carried out longer than about 70 seconds will gradually reach a point where it becomes an aerobic activity and will not produce significant strength gains. For the sake of simplicity, exercises for the upper torso should be done for a period of 60 seconds.

Each athlete should perform approximately 6-8 different MR exercises when lifting immediately after practice. The focal point of these exercises should be the major muscle groups. The major advantage of an MR workout is that it is time efficient — half the team exercises while the other half spots. If each exercise is to last 60 seconds and assuming the rest interval between exercises is minimal, a coach can strength train the entire team in as little as 15-20 minutes!

Your athletes should be paired according to size and strength. In addition, you should have a stopwatch and a whistle. Have half of your wrestlers go through the entire routine while you keep time and shout encouragement. Thereafter, the wrestlers would switch roles. Only one set of each exercise is necessary provided that your athletes train to the point where further repetitions are impossible.

The Lifter

As in lifting a barbell, the lifter should raise the resistance in a deliberate, controlled manner throughout the greatest possible range of motion (ROM) that safety allows. The athlete should raise the resistance (as supplied by the spotter) in about 1-2 seconds and return it to the stretched position in about 3-4 seconds. The lifters must keep their muscles loaded throughout the entire exercise — they should not relax until the movement is finished.

The Spotter

Since everyone is naturally stronger in some positions than in others due to changes in biomechanical leverage, the spotter is responsible for varying the resistance throughout the complete ROM. For example, everyone is a lot stronger in the lowering or "negative" phase of each exercise (perhaps due to internal muscular friction). So the spotter must apply more resistance during the negative phase of the repetition. The spotter must also regulate the resistance in accordance with the lifter's momentary level of strength. In brief, the spotter needs to furnish less resistance as the lifter fatigues during each exercise. Finally, the spotter must regulate the speed of movement such as requiring the lifter to raise the resistance in about 1-2 seconds and lower it in about 3-4 seconds.

EXERCISES

Space does not permit describing more than a few MR exercises. [Editor's note: Additional MR exercises will be discussed in the next chapter.} But here are a few to get you started.

Neck Flexion

This movement will strengthen your sternocleidomastoideus muscle on the front part of your neck. Sit down, bend your knees, place your feet flat on the mat and extend your neck backward (looking toward the ceiling). Put your hands beside your hips so that your palms are flat on the mat. The spotter should sit or kneel behind you and apply resistance against your chin with one hand and forehead with the other. To do the movement, pull your chin as close to your chest as possible to the mid-range position while the spotter offers resistance evenly throughout the full ROM. Pause briefly in this position and then resist as the spotter pulls your head back to the starting position (neck extended) to provide an adequate stretch.

Neck Extension

Your neck extensors and trapezius will be exercised with this movement. Assume a position on all fours and place your chin against your chest. The spotter should stand alongside your body, place one hand on your upper back and apply resistance against the back of your head. To perform the exercise, extend your neck backward as far as possible to the mid-range position while the spotter provides resistance evenly throughout the entire ROM. Pause momentarily in this position and then resist as the spotter pushes your head back to the starting position (chin on the chest) to ensure an adequate stretch.

Push-Up

This exercise will involve your chest, shoulders and triceps. Lay face down on the mat with your legs straight and your toes curled under your feet. Place your palms on the mat and spread your hands approximately shoulder-width apart. The spotter should straddle your body and apply resistance against your upper back. To do the movement, push up your body to the mid-range position until your elbows are just short of full extension as the spotter provides resistance evenly throughout the full ROM. Pause briefly in this position and then resist as the spotter pushes your body back to the starting position (chest on the mat) to obtain a sufficient stretch. When no further repetitions are possible, the spotter should prolong the exercise by pulling you to the mid-range position and then pushing you back to the starting position as you resist until 60 seconds of exercise have been completed.

ONE MORE REP

As you can see, a lack of equipment is no longer an obstacle in getting your athletes to strength train. Remember not to do any strength training within 48 hours of the match. Lastly, you can strength train immediately after practice but never immediately before practice.

Chapter 13
MORE MANUAL RESISTANCE

Partner-resisted — or manual resistance (MR) — exercises are an effective means of improving muscular strength when equipment is not available or when time is limited.

EXERCISES

Several MR exercises have been discussed previously. What follows are descriptions of four additional exercises. [Editor's note: Please refer to the previous chapter for the suggested guidelines and duties of the lifter and spotter.]

Seated Row

This exercise will strengthen your upper back, biceps and forearms. Sit down on the mat with your legs extended toward the spotter. Grasp a stick (or similar object) with your palms facing upward and spread your hands approximately shoulder-width apart. The spotter should sit down on the mat between your legs. The spotter should grasp the stick on the outside of your grip with the palms facing down. You should extend your arms fully and lean back slightly. To do the movement, pull the stick to the mid-range position until it touches your mid-section as the spotter provides resistance evenly throughout the full range of motion (ROM). Pause briefly in this position and then resist as the spotter pulls the stick back to the starting position (your arms fully extended) to ensure a sufficient stretch. Keep your torso relatively erect throughout this exercise — you should not bend backward at the waist. (If a stick or similar object is not available, your spotter and you can interlock your hands.)

Side Lateral Raise

Your shoulder muscles — specifically, your middle deltoid and trapezius — are strengthened with this movement. Stand upright with your arms hanging straight down and your palms facing your legs. Spread your feet apart a comfortable distance. The spotter should stand behind you and apply resistance against your lower arms. To perform the exercise, raise your arms away from the sides of your body to the mid-range position until they are parallel to the mat (keeping them fairly straight) as the spotter provides resistance evenly throughout the entire ROM. Pause momentarily in this position and then resist as the spotter pushes your arms back to the starting position (arms at your sides) to ensure an adequate stretch.

Seated Press

In addition to working your shoulder musculature, this exercise also involves your triceps. Sit down on the mat, bend your knees and place your feet flat on the mat. The spotter should stand behind you and place one leg against your back to provide support. Grasp a stick (or similar object) with your palms facing upward and spread your hands slightly wider than shoulder-width apart. Position the stick behind your neck on the upper part of your trapezius. The spotter should grasp the stick on the inside of your grip with the palms facing down. To do the movement, push up the stick to the mid-range position until your elbows are just short of full extension as the spotter offers resistance evenly throughout the full ROM. Pause briefly in this position and then resist as the spotter pushes the stick back to the starting position (stick on your trapezius) to provide a proper stretch. Again, if a stick or similar object is unavailable, you can interlock hands with your spotter.)

Sit-Up

This final exercise is an effective way of increasing the strength of your abdominals. Lay down on the mat with your knees bent, feet flat, chin tucked (head off the mat) and fingers interlocked behind your head. (Bending your knees and tucking your chin will minimize the strain on your lower back.) The angle between your upper and lower legs should be about 90 degrees. Fold your arms across your chest and lift your head off the mat. The upper portion of your shoulder blades should not touch the mat. The spotter should place the knees near the outside of your legs and apply resistance against the front part of your shoulders. (Your feet are between his knees.) To perform the exercise, bring your upper torso forward to the mid-range position until it is almost to your legs as the spotter provides resistance evenly throughout the entire ROM. Pause momentarily in this position and then resist as the spotter pushes your upper torso back to the starting position (shoulders near the mat) to obtain an adequate stretch. When no further repetitions are possible, the spotter should prolong the exercise by pulling you to the mid-range position and then pushing you back starting position as you resist until 60 seconds of exercise have been completed.

Chapter 14
GET A GRIP!

When I was the Assistant Strength and Conditioning Coach at Rutgers University in the mid 1980s, our wrestling team traveled to Florida to compete in the Sunshine Open. While in Florida, the team met an old friend of mine named Tom Laputka. Tom had played professional football for several years (in the Canadian Football League and the World Football League). He was a very powerful man — one of the world's first 500-pound bench pressers — and his gripping strength was legendary. When our team returned to New Jersey, I asked our Head Wrestling Coach, Deane Oliver, if Tom had a strong grip. Coach Oliver said, "Are you kidding? His grip could bring a grizzly bear to its knees!"

Indeed, a powerful grip is a sign of a powerful individual. On the wrestling mat, virtually every single offensive skill involves your grip strength — from sparring to completing a single-leg takedown to cradling your opponent. Defensively, grip strength is important in a number of skills including freeing yourself from your opponent's control. And in the weight room, your grip strength is involved in many multiple-joint movements that target your upper torso.

So the importance of having a strong grip is well established. Yet, very few athletes perform any type of direct work for their gripping muscles.

ANATOMY AND MUSCULAR FUNCTION

Your lower arm is made up of 19 different muscles with such exotic-sounding names as extensor carpi radialis brevis and flexor digitorum profundus. Fortunately, you will not need to have taken a course in Latin as it is well beyond the scope of the information presented here to discuss the muscles of your lower arm in such great detail. Instead, these muscles can simply be divided into two groups on the basis of their position and functions. The anterior group on the front part of your lower arm causes flexion and pronation (turning your palm downward); the posterior group on the back part of your lower arm causes extension and supination (turning the palm upward). These muscles affect your wrists and hands, which play a significant role in all tasks that involve gripping.

CONVENTIONAL METHODS

There are a few conventional methods — with barbells and dumbbells — that you can use to strengthen your grip. However, it is only necessary to perform one or two of these in any given workout. As a general guideline, you should reach muscular fatigue within about 8-12 repetitions.

Exercises

There are several basic grip-building exercises that can be done with conventional equipment. They are as follows:

1. **Wrist Flexion**. This exercise involves your wrist flexors on the front part of your lower arm. Grasp a barbell so that your hands are spaced about 4-6 inches apart with your palms facing upward and your thumbs alongside your fingers. In other words, your thumbs should be under the barbell next to your index fingers — that is, a "false grip." Your lower arms can be positioned directly over your upper legs or flat on the bench (between your legs). In this position, your lower arms should be roughly parallel to the floor. (This may require placing a pad underneath your feet.) Lean forward slightly so that the angle between your upper and lower arms is about 90 degrees or less. Your wrists should be directly over your kneecaps (or directly over the edge of the bench if you placed your lower arms on the bench). To do the exercise, pull the barbell up as high as possible to the mid-range position. Pause briefly in this position and then

lower the resistance under control to the starting position (wrists extended) at the end of each repetition to provide an adequate stretch. Do not throw the barbell by using your legs or by swinging your upper torso back and forth — movement should only occur around your wrist joints. Besides using a barbell, you can also do this exercise in a similar fashion using a dumbbell (one limb at a time), a machine (either selectorized or plate-loaded) or manual resistance.

2. **Wrist Extension**. This exercise involves your wrist extensors on the back part of your lower arm. Grasp a dumbbell so that your right palm is facing downward. Your right lower arm can be positioned directly over your right upper leg or flat on the bench (between your legs). In this position, your right lower arm should be roughly parallel to the floor. (This may require placing a pad underneath your foot.) Lean forward slightly so that the angle between your upper and lower arm is about 90 degrees or less. Your right wrist should be directly over your right kneecap (or directly over the edge of the bench if you placed your lower arm on the bench). To perform the exercise, pull the dumbbell up as high as possible to the mid-range position. Pause momentarily in this position and then lower the dumbbell under control to the starting position (wrist flexed) at the end of each repetition to provide an adequate stretch. After performing a set for your right lower arm, repeat the exercise for your left lower arm. Do not throw the dumbbell by using your legs or by swinging your upper torso back and forth — movement should only occur around your wrist joint. This exercise is more comfortable when it is performed one limb at a time with a dumbbell rather than both limbs at a time with a barbell. You can also do this exercise in a similar fashion using manual resistance.

3. **Finger Flexion**. This simple yet highly effective exercise isolates your finger flexors — important muscles that hardly anyone works directly. Grasp a dumbbell in each

hand with your arms straight and your palms facing the sides of your body. To do the exercise, pull the dumbbells up as high as possible to the mid-range position without using your arms — just your fingers. Pause briefly in this position — while squeezing the dumbbells as hard as possible — and then lower the dumbbells under control to the starting position (fingers extended) at the end of each repetition to provide an adequate stretch. Attempt to lower the dumbbells all the way down to your fingertips — to the point where the dumbbells almost drop from your fingers. Do not throw the weight by using your legs or by swinging your upper torso back and forth — movement should only occur around your finger joints. Besides using dumbbells, you can also do this exercise in a similar fashion using a barbell (with the bar in front of your body using either an overhand or an underhand grip), a selectorized machine (using a low pulley with a short bar attached to a cable) or manual resistance.

The Thick Bar

Another way for you to improve your grip strength is to use a thick bar or other unorthodox bar. A standard bar is about an inch or so in diameter. On the other hand, a thick or "fat" bar ranges anywhere from 2-3 inches in diameter. The extra-thick bar forces you to use your gripping muscles — specifically those in your lower arms, hands, wrists and fingers — to a much greater degree than a regular bar. Several productive exercises can be done with the thick bar including pressing and curling movements such as the bench press and bicep curl.

A specialized thick bar can also be fashioned from metal or heavy plastic tubing. Cut a piece that is about two feet in length and securely fasten a sturdy hook to its middle. This makeshift thick bar can then be attached to high and low pulleys and allow you to do a few additional exercises such as a seated row and lat pulldown. Another option is to purchase two pieces of heavy plastic tubing that are about six inches in length. You can slide these thick sleeves over the handles of many machine — such as a bench press, incline press, seated press and bicep curl — to create the effect of using a thick bar. Finally, one of the latest gadgets on the market is a special thick grip that can be quickly secured to dumbbell handles which again produces the effect of using a thick bar.

Whenever using a thick bar, make sure that you do not use a "false grip." In this case, it is important that you use your opposable thumbs!

UNCONVENTIONAL METHODS

You can also implement unconventional methods to strengthen your grip. From time to time, one or two of these activities can be performed to augment your workout. As a general guideline, perform each activity for about 60 seconds.

Ten Activities

There are a wide variety of unconventional activities for grip-building. These are ten more ways to strengthen your grip:

1. **Do wrist rollers.** This activity involves the use of a short bar with a rope or cable attachment. One end of the rope or cable is secured to the center of the bar and the other end to the resistance (which is usually weight plates). Stand upright with your arms straight and parallel to the ground. Then, simply "roll" the bar by flexing your lower arms in an alternating fashion. To make this activity progressively more challenging, you can increase the resistance or the length of the rope. For example, Bob Whelan — a Strength and Conditioning Coach in Washington, D.C. — has athletes stand on the roof of his building and do wrist rollers over the side using a rope that is 20 feet in length. But Jeff Watson — the Strength and Conditioning Coach at Villanova University — takes this activity to new heights: He has athletes do wrist rollers over the side of their football stadium using a 40-foot rope!

2. **Pinch grip plates.** To begin this activity, place two weight plates together with the smooth sides facing outward.

Grasp the plates with one hand such that your thumb is on one side and the rest of your fingers are on the other side. Grip the plates with the full length of your fingers and thumb. Pinch the plates together for as long as possible. Keep the plates from resting up against your body. Repeat the activity for the opposite side of your body. To make the activity progressively more difficult, you can use heavier/thicker plates or increase the duration of the hold.

3. **Climb a rope.** An activity that requires a great deal of grip strength (and skill) is rope climbing. This is especially true if you climb the rope without assistance from your hips and legs. To make this activity progressively more challenging, you can climb the rope with additional weight secured around your waist or in a backpack.

4. **Dry a towel.** After your workout, go into the locker room or bathroom and wet a large bath towel. Simply wring the towel as dry as possible by twisting and turning it with your hands. Rewet and repeat. Too easy? Try wringing out the towel without using your thumbs.

5. **Use a hand gripper.** A pair of hand grippers with lightweight, plastic handles are reasonably adequate but can break fairly easily with continued use. As your grip gets stronger, you will need to incorporate grippers with heavy-duty, iron handles (which come in varying levels of resistance). As a variation to doing repetitions, pinch a coin between the ends of the handles. See how long you can squeeze the handles together without dropping the coin. In fact, hold a dime between the handles and try to squeeze it into two nickels!

6. **Squeeze a ball.** This activity has its shortcomings in that the resistance is somewhat limited. Nevertheless, it makes for a great "finisher" at the end of a workout. You can either squeeze a rubber ball as hard as possible for 60 seconds or do 60 seconds worth of slow, deliberate repetitions.

7. **Hang from a chin bar.** Simply grasp a chin bar and hang onto it for as long as possible. To make this activity progressively more challenging, you can hang from the bar with additional weight secured around your waist or in a backpack.

8. **Grip a towel during chins.** Take a towel and wrap it once around the middle of a chin bar so that its ends are hanging straight down. Grasp the ends and pull yourself up as high as possible. Do as many repetitions as you can. To make this exercise progressively more challenging, you can pull yourself up with additional weight secured around your waist or in a backpack. Or, you can increase the number of repetitions.

9. **Pop bubble wrap.** This unique activity involves the use of bubble wrap that is often used in shipping packages. At the end of a workout, simply take a sheet of the bubble wrap and pop each of the bubbles by pressing your fingertips to your palms. Do not press with your thumbs — just use your four fingertips.

10. **Do the "Farmer's Walk."** Although this is a total-body movement, it is excellent for strengthening your grip. The so-called "Farmer's Walk" is not very complicated — just hold a dumbbell in each hand and start walking! You can perform this activity outdoors on a running track or indoors. For added pleasure, you can do the Farmer's Walk up and down stairs or stadium steps. Here is a possibility for you and a training partner: One wrestler starts by doing the Farmer's Walk around an outdoor track. When this wrestler can no longer hold onto the dumbbells, the partner takes over. Continue the Farmer's Walk around the track, taking turns carrying the dumbbells. As they say, "Misery loves company."

THOUGHTS ON WRIST STRAPS

Wrist straps are usually made out of a nylon and cotton blend. They are about 12-14 inches in length and about an inch in width. Wrist straps are used for assistance in holding onto a bar or a dumbbell when performing multiple-joint "pulling" movements for the upper torso.

Up until the end of 1990, I was adamantly opposed to using wrist straps. In the late 1970s and early 1980s, I was a powerlifter and the use of wrist straps was not allowed in competition. Plus, I felt that they provided artificial assistance. During the last few months of 1990, I was performing shoulder shrugs with dumbbells in my routine. In this exercise, I could not manage to do more than 13 repetitions with 100-pound dumbbells. Then, for whatever reason, I decided to do the exercise while wearing wrist straps. In that workout, I suddenly did 14 repetitions with 100-pound dumbbells. Six workouts later, I had progressed to 17 repetitions. Did my trapezius muscles suddenly get stronger? No, but the wrist straps allowed me to adequately work my trapezius by preventing my gripping muscles from fatiguing too quickly. Stated otherwise, without wrist straps I was underworking my trapezius.

Wrist straps should not be thought of as a replacement for doing exercises to strengthen your grip. However, they are certainly beneficial in exercises that are meant to address your larger muscle groups. Wrist straps may be warranted during the chin, lat pulldown, seated row, bent-over row, upright row, deadlift and shoulder shrug.

One of the most popular exercises in the weight room is the barbell squat. What follows are some of the most common questions that coaches and athletes ask about this movement.

Q: What is the advantage of doing the barbell squat?

A: Everything else being equal, the best exercises for increasing muscular size and strength are those that involve the greatest amounts of muscle mass. That said, one of the most productive exercises for the lower body is the barbell squat.

Q: Is there any disadvantage of doing the barbell squat?

A: Despite the all-important advantage of addressing an enormous amount of muscle tissue, the barbell squat has an inherent disadvantage in that many individuals — because of their body type and/or physical maturity — cannot perform the movement in a safe manner. Indeed, the orthopaedic concerns associated with the barbell squat have been voiced since at least the early 1960s. Since then, these concerns have been echoed by a number of highly regarded and experienced strength coaches at the scholastic, collegiate and professional levels.

Q: What are the specific concerns?

A: One orthopaedic concern is the knee. In order to maintain balance during the descending phase of the barbell squat, lifters must move their knees forward of their ankles. The farther the knee moves forward, the greater the stretch of the joint and the greater the shear (side-to-side) force at the patellar tendon. As the length of the legs increase, so does the distance that the knees move forward of the ankles. Therefore, someone with long legs is more prone to the shearing or "grinding" effect in the knees than someone with short legs.

Q: Can this shear force be eliminated or reduced?

A: To minimize the shear force in the knees during a barbell squat, you would have to maintain a position in which your lower legs — that is, your shin bones — are as close to perpendicular to the floor as possible. Unfortunately, this position cannot be attained because your center of gravity would drop outside your base of support and you would fall backward. However, this problem can be avoided by using what is known as a "safety squat bar." The bar has a heavily padded, "horse-collar" center yoke that — as oddly as it sounds — balances itself on your shoulders. This frees your hands so that you can hold onto the sides of a power rack while squatting. When doing squats in this manner, you can keep your lower legs roughly perpendicular to the floor without losing your balance and falling backward.

Q: Some of my wrestlers have told me that their lower backs hurt when they do barbell squats. What can I do to remedy this problem?

A: The lower back is actually a second area of orthopaedic concern. And the fact is that you might not be able to alleviate their low-back pain, especially if they have pre-existing low-back injuries or histories of low-back problems. Squatting with a barbell on the shoulders compresses the spinal column which, in extreme cases, could result in a herniated or ruptured disc. Compression is most evident when the lifter is in the bottom position of the barbell squat, where the anterior aspect of the lumbar vertebrae is compacted and the intervertebral discs are pushed in a posterior direction.

One study revealed that when doing barbell squats with as little as 0.8-1.6 times bodyweight, the load in the low-back region is actually 6-10 times bodyweight. This means that if you weigh 170 pounds and do barbell squats with about 135-270 pounds, the compressive load on your lumbar area can be anywhere from 1,020-1,700 pounds. The exact amount of loading is a function of how far the weight is from the lower back. Everything else being equal, someone with a long torso experiences higher compressive loads in the lower back than someone with a short torso.

To reduce the compressive loads, have your wrestlers minimize their trunk lean. In other words, instruct them not to bend forward excessively at the waist when they do their repetitions. Having them keep the bar lower on their shoulders rather than near or on the base of their necks will help reduce their forward lean.

Q: Can't you alleviate low-back pain by wearing a weightlifting belt?

A: A few studies have shown that wearing a weightlifting belt while squatting with a barbell increased intra-abdominal pressure which reduced the stress on the lower back. Wearing a weightlifting belt may also provide a psychological benefit.

Q: Are there any alternatives for those who cannot squat safely?

A: Fortunately, there are safer ways of addressing the extensive musculature of the lower body without the inherent risk of injury to the knees and lower back. First, be aware of the general body type that has a higher risk of injury from the barbell squat, namely individuals with relatively long legs and upper torsos. An excellent alternative for those with this body type — and others who cannot squat in a safe manner — is the leg press which is essentially the squatting motion without any vertical compression of the spine. In addition, you have the freedom to position your lower legs so that there is minimal shear force in your knees.

Q: Isn't there a difference between performing a squat with a barbell and doing a leg press with a machine?

A: In terms of your response, not much. The fact of the matter is that any exercise that progressively applies a load on the muscles will stimulate improvements in muscular size and strength. The barbell squat and the leg press address the same major muscles. In this case, it is the hips, quadriceps and hamstrings. Although the act of balancing free weights certainly requires a greater involvement of synergistic muscles, there's no evidence that this results in a significantly greater response. Indeed, studies have shown that there are no significant differences in the development of muscular size and strength when comparing groups who used free weights and groups who used machines.

The bottom line is that your muscles do not have eyes, brains or cognitive ability. Therefore, they cannot possibly know whether the source of resistance is a barbell, dumbbells, a selectorized machine, a plate-loaded machine or another human being. The sole factors that determine your response from strength training are your genetic makeup and your level of effort — not the equipment that you used.

Q: But isn't it better to do the barbell squat because it is ground-based training?

A: The notion of "ground-based training" has been receiving increased attention since the mid 1990s. Basically, ground-based training is the belief that since — for the most part — athletes compete with their feet in contact with the ground then that's how they should lift weights. In other words, it is the belief that all exercises should be done while standing. In response to this assertion, Jeff Watson — the Strength and Conditioning Coach at Villanova University — once asked, "Does this mean that you cannot get stronger while sitting or lying down?" Obviously, you *can* get stronger in an exercise even though it is not done in the standing position. Many wrestlers know this from personal experience because they have improved their strength in exercises that are performed while sitting or lying down such as the lat pulldown and bench press. So the notion that the barbell squat is better than the leg press because it is ground-based training is well meaning but without merit.

Q: What if I'm not the ideal body type to do the barbell squat but I do not have access to any other equipment to train my hip area?

A: If this is the case, your primary goal is to reduce the compressive loads and shear forces. You have at least two options for the barbell squat. One is to use a lighter weight and perform it with a speed of movement that is slower than that normally used. This will decrease the orthopaedic stress on your knees and lower back. A second option is to pre-fatigue your hips prior to doing the barbell squat. For example, you could do hip abduction using manual resistance with the aid of a partner. Once you finish this exercise, quickly move to the barbell squat. Because you pre-fatigued your hip area, you won't need to use as much weight as usual which will reduce the orthopaedic stress.

Q: For my wrestlers who can squat safely with a barbell, how often should they max out?

A: Often, workouts that incorporate the barbell squat — and other exercises for that matter — quickly morph into versions of a powerlifting contest with sets leading up to one-repetition maximum (1-RM) attempts. The focus on low-repetition sets with heavy weights usually leads to a greater reliance upon various supportive paraphernalia — such as knee wraps, squat suits and so on — which contribute less to the *development* of strength and more to the *demonstration* of strength. Any injuries that occur from this type of squatting are inexcusable. The squat can be a very productive exercise — but it does not have to be done like a competitive lift. Even if you have wrestlers who are also competitive powerlifters, they do not have to do low-repetition sets until they get close to a contest.

Q: So how many repetitions should they do?

A: Have your older wrestlers (juniors and seniors) use a repetition range of about 15-20; your younger wrestlers should use a slightly higher repetition range of about 20-25.

Q: Don't higher repetitions build muscular endurance instead of muscular strength?

A: It has been believed that doing higher repetitions (with a lighter weight) builds muscular endurance and doing lower repetitions (with a heavier weight) builds muscular strength. Actually, muscular endurance and muscular strength are directly related. If you increase your muscular endurance, you will also increase your muscular strength. Here's an example: Suppose that your 1-RM squat is 300 pounds and you can do 20 repetitions with 75% of your 1-RM (225 pounds). And after several months of strength training using high-repetition sets, suppose that you have progressed to the point where you can do 247.5 pounds for 20 repetitions. Given that you increased your performance in a 20-repetition squat by 10% — from 225 to 247.5 pounds — do you think that your 1-RM strength will be greater than, less than or equal to your previous 1-RM effort of 300 pounds? My guess is that it will be greater. So even though you trained with higher repetitions, your muscular strength increased.

By the way, it works the other way as well. If you increase your muscular strength, you will also increase your muscular endurance. Here's why: As you get stronger, you need fewer muscle fibers to sustain a sub-maximal effort (muscular endurance). This also means that you have a greater reserve available to extend the sub-maximal effort.

Q: How fast should the repetitions be done?

A: No one knows exactly how fast — or how slow — a repetition should be performed. But one study does offer some food for thought. A subject squatting with 80% of his four-repetition maximum incurred a 225-pound peak shearing force during a repetition that took 4.5 seconds to complete and a 270-pound peak shearing force during a repetition that took 2.1 seconds to complete. This is clear evidence that slower speeds of movement reduce the shear force on joints.

Q: Should my wrestlers lock their knees between repetitions?

A: No. There are two reasons why they should not "lock" or completely extend their knees. First of all, it unloads their muscles which makes the exercise less effective. Second, it increases their risk of hyperextending their knee joints which makes the exercise more dangerous.

Q: *How deep should you go during the squat?*

A: For the most part, you need only squat to a depth in which your upper legs are approximately parallel to the ground.

Q: *How can I reach this depth in the squat without losing my balance?*

A: If you cannot squat to a point where your upper legs are parallel to the ground, it may be because your stance is too narrow. Spread your feet slightly wider than shoulder-width apart. Also, keep your toes pointed outward slightly. These suggestions should help you attain a proper depth. By the way, a narrow stance will also increase your trunk lean as you squat which will, in turn, increase the compressive load on your lower back.

Q: *Is it okay for me to bounce out of the bottom position of the squat?*

A: No it is not. Bouncing out of the bottom position produces higher compressive loads and shear forces.

Q: *What do you think about wearing knee wraps while squatting?*

A: Having been a competitive powerlifter, I am not convinced that knee wraps provide any significant advantage in safeguarding the knees against injury. By tightly wrapping their knees, lifters get an artificial boost out of the bottom position of the squat which allows them to use much more weight than normal. This, however, relates more to *demonstrating* strength rather than to *developing* it. To build functional strength in your hip and leg musculature, you would be better off not using knee wraps or other forms of synthetic support (such as squat suits).

Chapter 16
WRESTLING CAMP Q & A

The Princeton University Wrestling Camp — directed by Head Coach Michael New — was held from July 9-13, 2000. One evening, I had the pleasure of speaking to the campers about strength and conditioning for wrestling. A question-and-answer session proved to be quite popular. What follows is a sampling of questions that the wrestlers asked about strength and conditioning along with my responses.

Q: *What should our diets consist of?*

A: To obtain credible information on nutrition, you should not go to a GNC Store. Nor should you ask individuals who are willing to give you the "secret" to good nutrition only later try to sell you a product or a book or a supplement. The people that you should seek for legitimate nutritional information are registered dieticians. The information that I'm about to tell you is consistent with what you would hear from the majority of registered dieticians and others who are not trying to take money out of your pocket. Most of your calories should be in the form of carbohydrate. That's your body's preferred fuel during intense activity. At least 65% of your calories should be from carbohydrate. Roughly 15% of your calories should come from protein and no more than 20% from fat.

Q: *So how much protein do I need?*

A: The Recommended Dietary Allowance (RDA) for protein is 0.8 grams per kilogram of bodyweight per day. If you do not know your bodyweight in kilograms, simply divide your weight in pounds by 2.2. So if you are 220 pounds, you weigh 100 kilograms. To determine your RDA for protein, multiply your bodyweight in kilograms by 0.8. In this example, you would need about 80 grams of protein per day. Since there are four calories in a gram of protein, this is the equivalent of about 320 calories coming from protein. Research has established the fact that individuals who are involved in rigorous training — either strength training or endurance training — require a bit more than the RDA. For these individuals, the amount of daily protein intake appears to be about 1.5-2.0 grams per kilogram of bodyweight per day. However, this increased protein requirement is usually met through a regular diet without any need for additional supplementation.

Q: I have heard some people recommend two sets of an exercise and others three sets. What do you think?

A: The number of sets that should be done for each exercise is a hotly debated topic. For years, it was generally accepted that performing multiple sets of an exercise was better than single sets. Two researchers from Adelphi University — Dr. Ralph Carpinelli and Dr. Robert Otto — did a comprehensive literature review of all relevant research that examined different numbers of sets. Their review showed that there were no significant differences between single- and multiple-set training in 33 of 35 studies that dated back to 1956. In a later review, Dr. Carpinelli noted two additional studies that found no significant differences between single- and multiple-set training. That's a total of 35 of 37 studies in which one set of an exercise produced results that were not significantly different from multiple sets. Having trained collegiate wrestlers since the early 1980s, I think that single sets done to muscular fatigue are just as effective as multiple sets in terms of increasing muscular size and strength.

Q: After you do a workout of one set per exercise, is it okay to go back and repeat it again?

A: Assuming that you did each set to the point of muscular fatigue, there's really no benefit in doing it again. I'm not saying that you cannot; I'm just saying that if you train to exhaustion, it is not really necessary to do more than one set of an exercise.

Q: What do you think of the Jammer™ for building explosiveness?

A: Well, you might be able to demonstrate more explosiveness when performing the Jammer™, but that does not necessarily mean that this explosiveness will transfer or "carry over" to the wrestling mat. That also goes for other exercises done in an explosive fashion, by the way. As a side note, the Jammer™ is one of many devices that have been promoted for what's become known as "ground-based training." If you are not familiar with the term, ground-based training is the notion that since — for the most part — athletes compete with their feet in contact with the ground then that's how they should lift weights. In other words, it is the belief that all exercises should be done while standing. This suggests that any exercise done in a seated or lying position is utterly worthless including the bench press, incline press, lat pulldown, seated row, seated press, leg press, leg extension, leg curl and abdominal crunch. Since the dip and chin are not done with the feet in contact with the ground, the theory of ground-based training implies that these two movements are also useless. Obviously, you can get stronger in all of the aforementioned exercises and others even though they are not done in the standing position with the feet in contact with the ground. Many of you know that from personal experience because you have improved your strength in those exercises. So the notion of ground-based training is well meaning but without merit.

Q: What should I eat right before I lift?

A: Actually, I do not think that you should eat anything right before you lift. If you are going to be training in an intense fashion — and you should — any food intake prior to your workout could lead to stomach upset and/or nausea.

Q: My left shoulder hurts when I do tricep extensions. What's wrong?

A: I'm not sure what's wrong with your shoulder but if a joint hurts when you do an exercise then the exercise should be modified or eliminated. And let's distinguish between muscle pain and joint pain. Generally speaking, muscle pain is okay. That just means you are working hard. On the other hand, joint pain is not okay. That means you may very well have an orthopaedic problem. If that's the case, you should consult with certified sportsmedical personnel. In terms of the tricep extension, try decreasing the weight that you normally use and do the movement more slowly. This will reduce the orthopaedic stress. If that does not work, try doing the exercise one arm at a time. Or use a different exercise for your triceps. But if joint pain is present in any exercise for your triceps — or other body parts — you should eliminate that exercise from your routine. Remember, the key is to do pain-free exercise.

Q: *What do you think about energy bars?*

A: First, keep in mind that use of the term "energy" can be misleading. Numerous products use the word "energy" in their name. This suggests that the product will improve your stamina or make you more energetic. In truth, calories provide you with energy and three nutrients provide you with calories: carbohydrate, protein and fat. In short, we get energy from food. So technically, a can of soda is an "energy drink," a hot dog is an "energy roll," a pad of butter is an "energy stick," a slice of bacon is an "energy strip," a chocolate chip cookie is an "energy disc" and an ice cream sandwich is an "energy bar." At any rate, there's nothing inherently wrong with most of the products that have been dubbed "energy bars." So it is okay if you want to eat energy bars — especially when it is more convenient for you because of time constraints. Just do not make them the focal point of your food intake. Remember, there's nothing wrong with energy bars . . . but there's nothing magical about them, either.

Q: *What about creatine?*

A: Creatine has received much attention in the athletic community and the media. There are many anecdotal reports that creatine works but scientific research paints a different picture. The majority of studies on creatine have been conducted in a controlled, laboratory setting. Some of these studies have shown that creatine enhances performance. However, most of those studies have examined performance on a stationary cycle. That would be great if there were competitions in stationary cycling. But there are not. There also have been studies conducted on creatine outside a laboratory setting that examined performance in activities that are more specific to real-life athletics such as running and swimming. In virtually every study conducted outside the laboratory, there were no performance enhancements associated with creatine supplementation. In some instances, performance actually worsened.

From a safety standpoint, understand that the long-term risks of using creatine are unknown. It is thought that potential side effects include weight gain (most likely from water retention), diarrhea and muscle cramping. Based upon the scientific information that is available at this point in time, I would not want my son to take creatine. If you do decide to use creatine, make sure that you do not exceed the recommended dosages that are indicated on the label.

Q: What's your opinion on doing the seated press and lat pulldown behind the head?

A: This is a great topic for discussion. Many in the sportsmedical community avoid prescribing either of those exercises. The reason is that there is more orthopaedic stress in the shoulder joint when a bar is pressed or pulled behind the head rather than in front. The best description is a tightness or a pinching in the shoulder joint. My position is that these exercises are acceptable as long as a person can do them in a pain-free fashion. If not, then the exercises should be removed from your program and replaced with alternatives that are orthopaedically acceptable.

Q: Does chromium melt fat?

A: Well, fat can certainly melt. But in order to do so, your body temperature would be so high that your brain would boil and your blood would probably coagulate. To answer your question, though, the supplement chromium does not melt fat. Nor does it promote fat loss in any way.

Chapter 17
IMPROVING SKILLS:
WHAT THE RESEARCH SAYS

The science of motor learning is the study of muscular movement or, simply, "motor skills." Research in this discipline promotes an understanding of how skills are learned, applied and refined. The intent to expedite the acquisition of skills has given rise to a number of practices that are well meaning but are generally unsupported by the motor-learning literature.

SKILLS AND ABILITIES

Though the terms are often used interchangeably and are somewhat related, skills are vastly different from abilities. A skill refers to the level of performance in one specific action. Skills can be modified and improved through practice. On the other hand, an ability refers to a general trait. This includes dynamic strength, static strength, explosive strength, speed of limb movement, quickness, coordination, dynamic balance, static balance and stamina. Abilities are thought to be genetically determined and, unlike skills, cannot be changed by practice or experience. Abilities are not specific skills in themselves. However, abilities are factors that determine performance potential and form the foundation of a number of specific wrestling skills. For example, performing a distinct skill such as a single-leg takedown requires the general underlying abilities of explosive strength, speed of limb movement, quickness and coordination.

Quickness Exercises

Being "quick" is obviously advantageous in the sport of wrestling. General "quickening" drills are frequently used with the expectation that the movement patterns learned in those exercises will transfer to specific wrestling skills and thus improve performance. Numerous studies have investigated the possibility of transferring quickness to other skills. According to Richard Schmidt, Ph.D., there is little evidence that practicing a skill that requires a certain ability — such as quickness — will improve another skill that requires the same abilities. Dr. Schmidt suggests that there are at least three separate abilities that are used to act quickly: (1) reaction time (the interval of time between an unanticipated stimulus and the start of the response); (2) response orientation (where one of many stimuli is presented, each of which requires its own response); and (3) speed of movement (the interval of time between the start of a movement and its completion). Each of these three abilities involves quickness. However, these three abilities are separate and independent of each other. Studies have reported no transfer effect from quickening exercises to a motor task requiring quickness. Other research has shown that reaction time and speed of movement have essentially no correlation — that is, the abilities have very little in common. Therefore, being "quick" depends upon the circumstances under which speedy responses are required.

Similar findings have been reported in a number of other studies. With very few exceptions, the correlations among motor tasks are very low. In short, there is no general ability for quickness or anything else. It would not be expected that an ability such as quickness could be improved by practice anyway.

THE TRANSFER OF LEARNING

The transfer of learning refers to the effects of past learning upon the acquisition of a new skill. Many individuals take the transfer of learning for granted. They assume that movements for the execution of one skill always and automatically transfer or "carry over" to the learning of another.

Types of Transfer

The truth of the matter is that the acquisition of skills can be enhanced or impaired depending upon the correct use of the transfer of learning principles. The transfer of learning from one skill to another may be positive, negative or absent altogether. Positive transfer occurs when the influence of prior learning facilitates the learning of a new skill. Negative transfer happens when the learning of a new skill inhibits the learning of a second skill. No transfer occurs if the learning of one skill has a negligible influence on the learning of a second skill.

THE USE OF WEIGHTED OBJECTS

It is widely believed that using weighted implements contributes to the learning of specific motor patterns and sports skills. This has led to the practice of trying to simulate sports skills in the weight room using a variety of weighted objects. In the motor-learning literature, practicing a particular motor skill with weighted implements is known as "overload training." Barbells, dumbbells, medicine balls and other weighted objects are used during overload training with the expectation of improving performance.

The basis for mimicking sports skills with weighted implements is entirely anecdotal, having very little support from the motor-learning literature. There is no research evidence suggesting that basic movement patterns can be transferred from task to task. Yet, many individuals still insist that the use of certain weightlifting movements encourages a positive transfer of motor ability to the athletic arena. If there were a correlation between weightlifting skills and other sports skills, then highly successful weightlifters would excel at literally every sports-related movement that they attempted. And we know that this is not true.

The Kinesthetic Aftereffect

Motor-learning research refers to a "kinesthetic aftereffect," which is defined by George Sage, Ph.D., as a "perceived modification in the shape, size or weight of an object . . . as a result of experience with a previous object." Athletes experience the kinesthetic aftereffect during overload training. This phenomenon is exemplified by a person who runs with a weighted vest followed by the perceived ability to run faster after the vest is removed. Essentially, the kinesthetic aftereffect is nothing more than a sensory illusion.

Research indicates that the kinesthetic aftereffect is not accompanied by a measurable improvement in performance in the skills that have been practiced using weighted objects. One study reported no significant changes in the speed of movement during elbow flexion immediately following the application of overload. Another study had subjects perform vertical jumps with a weighted vest, followed by jumps without the weight. The researchers found no improvements in vertical-jump performance after the overload practices. Nearly identical results have been reported in many other studies.

Dr. Sage suggests that "any attempt to improve performance by utilizing objects that are slightly heavier than normal while practicing gross motor skills that will be later used in sports competition seems to be hardly worth the time spent and the money paid for the weighted objects." Dr. Schmidt adds, "Teaching a particular Skill A simply because you would like it to transfer to Skill B, which is of major interest, is not very effective, especially if you consider the time spent on Skill A that could have been spent on Skill B instead."

Problems with Using Weighted Objects

According to Wayne Westcott, Ph.D., four problems occur when practicing sports skills with weighted objects. The problem areas relate to neuromuscular confusion, incorrect movement speed, orthopedic stress and insufficient workload.

Neuromuscular confusion. Attempting to duplicate a wrestling skill with a weight or a weighted implement is a gigantic step in the wrong direction. Each time that you perform a given wrestling skill, there is a specific neuromuscular pattern involved that is unique to that movement alone. Introducing anything foreign to the "pattern" — such as weighted vests, ankle weights, barbells or medicine balls — will only serve to confuse your original neuromuscular pathways, actually creating a negative transfer and a resultant decrease in performance. Watch someone attempt to mimic a sports skill with a weighted object and you will quickly notice that the effort used to direct the unfamiliar weight results in a different movement pattern that is labored and awkward. In reality, it is a very different motion altogether.

Incorrect movement speed. If a wrestling skill is to be performed at a given speed, it should be practiced at that speed in order to facilitate the learning of the skill. Practicing a wrestling skill at a slower or a faster speed than actually would be used in the performance of the skill will cause a momentary negative transfer. On a related note, Thomas Pipes, Ph.D., suggests that running with ankle weights will train the neuromuscular system at slower speeds and can cause a person to actually run more slowly. The same negative effects are produced when running with a parachute or while pulling a sled.

Orthopedic stress. Another problem associated with practicing a wrestling skill with a weighted object pertains to the stresses that are placed on the joints. Practicing with implements that are heavier than usual can place considerable orthopedic stress on the involved body parts and is dangerous. Structural stress is most evident in the shoulder, elbow and wrist.

Insufficient workload. Another reason why weighted objects do not enhance wrestling performance is that they do not increase strength in the involved musculature. The added resistance provided by a weighted object is not sufficient enough to surpass the "threshold" for strength development. The added resistance is a mere fraction of what is necessary to overload your muscles.

SPECIFICITY VERSUS GENERALITY

The Principle of Specificity states that activities must be specific to an intended skill in order for a maximal transfer of learning — or carryover — to occur. Specific means "exact" or "identical," not "similar" or "just like." Indeed, one researcher has stated that "transfer is highly specific and occurs only when the practiced movements are identical."

Movement patterns for different skills are never executed exactly alike. One researcher has noted that very similar-appearing motor skills are based upon very different patterns of muscular activity. According to Dr. Schmidt, some movement patterns — although they outwardly appear to use the same muscular actions — are actually quite different and require learning and practice of each task separately.

Power Cleans

Power cleans have long been touted as being specific to an incredibly wide range of skills, from the breaststroke to the golf swing to the double-leg takedown. How is it possible that any one movement could be identical to such a broad group of differing skills? Answer: It cannot.

In one study, subjects performed elbow flexion — that is, a bicep curl — in the standing position. After training, elbow-flexion strength had increased considerably when measured in the standing position. However, similar movements in an unfamiliar position (supine) revealed only a slight increase in strength. In other words, a standing bicep curl is not even specific to a nearly identical exercise such as a supine bicep curl. Likewise, a power clean is not specific to any other similar lifting movement — such as an upright row. A power clean is even less similar to athletic skills and, therefore, is not specific to any athletic skill. In terms of a power clean being specific to another athletic skill, John Jesse, RPT, asked, "What other activity requires lifting a heavy weight to the shoulders?"

So, performing power cleans may be similar to performing a vertical jump and doing lunges may be just like executing a single-leg takedown, but the truth is that power cleans will only help you get better at doing power cleans and lunges will only help you get better at doing lunges. Similarly, heaving medicine balls around is great for improving your skill at heaving medicine balls around and nothing else. Also, jumping off wooden boxes will only perfect your skill at jumping off wooden boxes. There is no exercise done in the weight room — with barbells or machines — that will expedite the learning of wrestling skills. Fred Allman, M.D., has stated that the performance of Olympic-style weightlifting movements provide little benefit to athletes in training programs other than the sport of Olympic-style weightlifting.

In addition, a power clean is an extremely complex motor skill. Like any other motor skill, it takes a lot of time and patience to master its specific neuromuscular pattern. This valuable time and energy could be used more effectively elsewhere — such as perfecting specific wrestling skills and techniques that will actually be used on the mat.

Elements of Specificity

There are four elements of specificity that define the rules for determining whether or not two movements are specific:

- **Muscle specificity.** The exact muscle(s) used in the exercise must also be used in the athletic skill.
- **Movement specificity.** The exact movement pattern used in the exercise must be the same as the athletic skill.
- **Speed specificity.** The speed of movement used in the exercise must be identical to the athletic skill.
- **Resistance specificity.** The precise resistance used in the exercise must be identical to the external resistance encountered in the athletic skill.

In order for a weight-training exercise to be specific to a wrestling skill, all four of these elements would have to be true. One skill may resemble another in terms of identical muscle(s), movement pattern, speed of movement and resistance used. However, at best a weight-training exercise can only approximate a wrestling skill . . . it cannot duplicate it.

IMPROVING WRESTLING SKILLS

The acquisition and improvement of wrestling skills is a process in which an athlete develops a set of responses into an integrated and organized movement pattern. Two requirements are necessary in order for you to increase your efficiency at performing wrestling skills: practicing the skill and strengthening the muscles.

Practicing the Skill

The first requirement for improving your wrestling skills is to literally practice the intended skill for thousands and thousands of task-specific repetitions. Each repetition must be done with perfect technique so that its specific movement pattern becomes firmly ingrained in your "motor memory." The skill must be practiced perfectly and exactly as it would be used on the mat. Further, the skill should not be practiced with weighted implements.

Strengthening the Muscles

The second requirement for improving your wrestling skills is to strengthen the major muscle groups that are used during the performance of a particular skill. Strength training should not be done in a manner that mimics or apes a particular wrestling skill so as not to confuse or impair the intended movement pattern. A stronger muscle can produce more force; if you can produce more force, you will require less effort and be able to perform the skill more quickly, more accurately and more efficiently. But again, this is provided that you have practiced enough in a correct manner so that you will be more skillful in applying that force. Remember, practice makes perfect . . . but only if you practice perfect.

SPORT-SPECIFIC EXERCISES

Are there sport-specific exercises? Should a wrestler perform different exercises than a football player or a swimmer? Each athlete has the same muscles that function in the same manner as any other athlete. For example, your biceps flex your lower arm around your elbow joint. The same is true for a diver, a shot putter, a quarterback, a lacrosse player and a defensive lineman. It follows then that there is no such thing as a sport-specific exercise. As a wrestler, you need to perform certain movements as a precaution to prevent an injury to a joint that receives a great deal of stress such as exercises for your neck — exercises that other athletes might not need to perform. You should also do exercises for your grip strength — exercises that other athletes might not need to perform. Other than that, you should select movements that exercise your muscles in the safest and most efficient way possible. Remember, skill training is *specific* to wrestling but strength training is *general*. In other words, the *development* of strength is general but the *application* of strength is specific.

Chapter 18

I KNOW WHAT YOU DID
LAST SUMMER

A number of years ago on a September afternoon, a collegiate wrestler who was entering his senior year came into the weight room for a workout. I had not seen him since he left campus in May, so I was quite anxious to learn how much progress he had made over the summer. His first exercise was the leg press in which he did about 20 repetitions to muscular fatigue. Immediately following this, I assisted him with several "negatives" in which I lifted the weight (the concentric part) and he lowered the weight (the negative part). Less than a minute later — without doing another exercise — he vomited. Over the years, I had seen many highly conditioned athletes lift weights with so much aggressiveness and intensity that they vomited at some point during their workouts. Needless to say, it was unusual for someone to do so after the first exercise. I asked the wrestler if he was sick and he said, "No, I just didn't train all summer." This was as unfortunate as it was incredulous since he essentially gave his opponents a four-month head start on the upcoming season. And a Division I athlete cannot afford to do that and expect to be competitive. When wrestling against this unprepared athlete early in the school year, a teammate who had trained religiously for the upcoming season might think, "I know what you did last summer" followed quickly by "Nothing."

Compare this to the dedicated effort of Princeton University's Ryan Bonfiglio, a senior co-captain of the 2000-01 team who wrestled at 165 pounds. Ryan was not exactly a "blue chip" wrestler when he came out of high school. In fact, his greatest wrestling accomplishment as a senior was finishing second in districts (in Pennsylvania). But a few summers ago, he raised his commitment to the sport of wrestling to a new level. In Ryan's case, the follow-up to the statement "I know what you did last summer" was "You prepared for wrestling." The changes that he made — both physically as well as mentally — were simply staggering. Ryan's muscular strength and cardiovascular conditioning improved dramatically as did his lean-body (muscle) mass. To put it bluntly and succinctly, he became a complete stud. Ryan was also much more focused on the mat, becoming a real student of wrestling. This past season, he was rewarded for his efforts by finishing second in the Eastern Intercollegiate Wrestling Association (EIWA) tournament — losing by a score of 4-2 in the finals — and being one of three Princeton wrestlers to qualify for the 2001 NCAA Championships. (The other two were junior Juan Venturi at 133 pounds and sophomore Greg Parker at 174 pounds.) Ryan's wrestling portfolio for this season also includes a victory over a tough Matt Lackey of Illinois at the North Carolina State Duals by a score of 3-2. (An outstanding athlete and two-time state champion in high school, Matt placed third at this year's NCAA Championships.)

WHY THE SUMMER?

I cannot overemphasize the fact that in order to realize your potential as a wrestler, it is an absolute necessity that you continue your training over the summer months. But why is the summer so important in this regard? In general, it is arguably the best possible time to prepare for the upcoming season. Michael New — the fiery Wrestling Coach at Princeton University — states, "The summer is a low-key time to begin healthy nutritional habits and lifestyle changes."

More specifically, you can increase your level of strength and conditioning a considerable amount over the course of the summer. And this can help you significantly on the mat. Case in point: Ryan's newfound strength and conditioning that he developed during the summer months allowed him to do things on the mat that were previously difficult — if not impossible — to accomplish.

In addition, consistent training during the summer can help

you to manage your bodyweight at desirable levels. Hey, it is not in your best interests — or that of your team — to return to school from the summer at whatever bodyweight the scale happens to read. One of the most important things that Ryan did over the summer was to take the discipline required in making weight and use it to his advantage. How? Simple. First, he improved his nutritional habits by consuming a moderate amount of calories and low-fat foods. Second, he coupled this with an extremely intense and demanding regimen of strength training and conditioning. The result was a decrease in body fat and an increase in muscle mass. In 1997-98, Ryan wrestled as a small 142-pounder; in 1998-99 — after a summer of dedicated effort — he wrestled as a strapping 165-pounder. This remarkable physical renovation was underscored in October 1998 when one of our athletic trainers measured Ryan's body fat at less than 6% at a body weight of about 170 pounds. (One other quick note of interest: As a 142-pounder, Ryan's record was 13-14; in his first season as a 165-pounder, he recorded more than 30 wins.)

What else can be done during the summer? One of the biggest things that you can do is to practice and perfect your skills and, perhaps, compete in a tournament or two. Last summer, for instance, Matt Lackey was not idle. He won the 167.5-pound title at the FILA Freestyle National Championships and World Team Trials and competed at the World Championships in Nantes, France. Now that is a productive summer!

Finally, at the end of the season you can review your performance and revise previous goals for the next season. Then, you can use the summer months as a springboard to help realize those goals. Last year, maybe your primary goal was to make the varsity team. Next year, your revised goal should be loftier — maybe to place in the top three in districts. Regardless of whatever goals you set, make sure that they are challenging yet realistic.

THE BOTTOM LINE

The first time that you roll around on the mat with your teammates in the fall, make sure you prepared so well that each one thinks, "I know what you did last summer" followed quickly by "You prepared for wrestling."

Have a healthy and productive summer!

Chapter 19

SUMMER CONDITIONING PROGRAM FOR WRESTLING

In order to effectively prescribe a conditioning program, coaches must identify the major energy system(s) utilized to perform a given sport or activity. Basically, there are three metabolic systems available. Two of these do not require the presence of oxygen and are termed "anaerobic"; the other can only operate in the existence of oxygen and is labeled "aerobic." Your two anaerobic energy systems are the Phosphagen (or ATP-PC) System and the Lactic-Acid System (Anaerobic Glycolysis); your aerobic source is known as the Oxygen (or Aerobic) System.

Since the primary energy system(s) for an activity can be estimated on the basis of performance time, it follows that the short-term, high-intensity efforts of a wrestler primarily require the use of the anaerobic pathways, namely the ATP-PC and Lactic-Acid Systems. Thus, a training regimen for wrestling should strive to develop the physiological capacities of these particular systems.

PROGRAM ORGANIZATION

The main purpose of a conditioning program is to progressively overload the energy systems required for wrestling, thereby stimulating biomechanical adaptations that are specific to the sport. Accordingly, this program is divided into three distinct phases which emphasize the various energy systems: (1) aerobic; (2) anaerobic and aerobic; and (3) anaerobic. Briefly, the 12-week program consists of three weekly workouts to be performed every other day. A summary of the program is provided in Figure 1.

Phase I: Aerobic

Regardless of the major metabolic system(s) necessary to perform a given sport, a properly organized conditioning program should begin with an aerobic phase to overload the oxygen consumption, transportation and utilization mechanisms in order to build a base of support. Once a solid aerobic foundation has been established through long-duration efforts, anaerobic work may start gradually.

This four-week phase begins with a 12-minute run to assess each athlete's initial level of conditioning. The next workout is a 2,800-meter run (roughly 1.75 miles). Thereafter, the prescription for each session alternates times and distances according to the goal. The times and the distances increase by one minute and 200 meters per week, respectively.

Phase II: Anaerobic and Aerobic

The anaerobic and aerobic energy systems are integrated in this four-week phase of conditioning during which interval training is introduced. Various training methods can be considered as interval training, in which repeated bouts of high-intensity exercise are alternated with periods of relief — such as a walk or slow jog — until the prescription is completed. Prescriptions differ in the distance of the work intervals, the length and type of the relief intervals and the number of repetitions of work intervals.

Intermittent periods of work and relief permit a partial recovery of the anaerobic energy systems which are normally exhausted in a relatively short period of time during a continuous effort. Therefore, interval training allows an athlete to work at a higher intensity for a longer duration with less physiological stress by delaying the onset of fatigue associated with anaerobic activities.

Specific interval workouts are detailed in Figure 2. Please note that a prescription described as "8 x 100 (300)" means that eight 100-meter sprints are to be performed with a 300-meter jog during each relief interval. That is, the athlete sprints 100 meters, jogs 300 meters, sprints 100 meters, jogs 300 meters and so on. (Note: If jogging slowly during the relief interval is too demanding, walking may be done instead.)

Phase III: Anaerobic

During this four-week phase of training, the anaerobic pathways are effectively overloaded in order to develop the ATP-PC System. This is accomplished by repeating sprints at maximal speed. Long-distance running should be continued throughout this phase once per week to maintain an aerobic base.

Figure 3 lists specific sprint routines. A prescription of "4 x 150 (150)" means that four 150-meter sprints are to be executed with a 150-meter walk between each sprint.

This summer conditioning program can be repeated again once the 12 weeks are complete. However, since an aerobic foundation has already been established, there is no need to repeat the first four weeks of the training program.

SUMMARY

Your athletes will be better able to recover and withstand the rigors of practice and competition when they develop the specific metabolic pathways involved in wrestling. Additionally, a conditioning program represents an excellent way of keeping the bodyweight at desirable levels during the off-season. Brief sessions of high-intensity strength training should also be performed three times weekly in conjunction with this or any other conditioning program.

FIGURE 1: Summer Conditioning Program		
Phase 1: Aerobic (weeks 1-4)		
WEEK	**WORKOUT**	**PRESCRIPTION**
1	1	12:00 run (test)
1	2	2,800-meter run
1	3	12:00 run
2	4	3,000-meter run
2	5	13:00 run
2	6	3,000-meter run
3	7	14:00 run
3	8	3,200-meter run
3	9	14:00 run
4	10	3,400-meter run
4	11	15:00 run
4	12	3,400-meter run
Phase 2: Anaerobic and Aerobic (weeks 5-6)		
5	13	16:00 run
5	14	3,600-meter run
5	15	3,600-meter intervals*
6	16	17:00 run
6	17	3,800-meter run
6	18	3,800-meter intervals*
7	19	18:00 run
7	20	4,000-meter run
7	21	4,000-meter intervals*
8	22	19:00 run
8	23	4,200-meter run
8	24	4,200-meter intervals*
Phase 3: Anaerobic (weeks 9-12)		
9	25	20:00 run
9	26	sprints**
9	27	4,400-meter intervals*
10	28	21:00 run
10	29	sprints**
10	30	4,600-meter intervals*
11	31	22:00 run
11	32	sprints**
11	33	4,800-meter intervals*
12	34	23:00 run
12	35	sprints**
12	36	5,000-meter intervals*

*See Figure 2 for specific interval workouts

** See Figure 3 for specific sprint workouts

FIGURE 2: Specific Interval Workouts			
WEEK	WORKOUT	PRESCRIPTION	DISTANCE
5	15	1 x 200 (200) 8 x 100 (300)	3,600
6	18	1 x 200 (200) 8 x 100 (300) 1 x 100 (100)	3,800
7	21	2 x 200 (200) 8 x 100 (300)	4,000
8	24	2 x 200 (200) 8 x 100 (300) 1 x 100 (100)	4,200
9	27	3 x 200 (200) 8 x 100 (300)	4,400
10	30	3 x 200 (200) 8 x 100 (300) 1 x 100 (100)	4,600
11	33	4 x 200 (200) 8 x 100 (300)	4,800
12	36	4 x 200 (200) 8 x 100 (300) 1 x 100 (100)	5,000

The workout distance includes the length of the jog between intervals.

FIGURE 3: Specific Sprint Workouts			
WEEK	WORKOUT	PRESCRIPTION	DISTANCE
9	26	4 x 150 (150) 6 x 100 (100) 8 x 40 (40) 8 x 10 (10)	1,600
10	29	5 x 150 (150) 6 x 100 (100) 9 x 40 (40) 9 x 10 (10)	1,800
11	32	5 x 150 (150) 8 x 100 (100) 9 x 40 (40) 9 x 10 (10)	2,000
12	35	6 x 150 (150) 8 x 100 (100) 10 x 40 (40) 10 x 10 (10)	2,200

The workout distance does not include the length of the walk between sprints.

Chapter 20
STEROID USE:
HISTORY AND PREVALENCE

The problem of substance abuse is ever-present in today's society. Nowadays, you can hardly read a newspaper, listen to a radio or watch a television without being informed of the latest drug-related incidents. Substance abuse has also begun to infect many aspects of athletic competition with increasing regularity. This problem gained worldwide attention during the 1988 Summer Olympics in Seoul. Ten athletes were disqualified from competition after testing positive for one or more banned substances — mostly steroids, amphetamines and diuretics. The disqualification of Canadian Ben Johnson — a gold-medalist sprinter — shocked the entire globe. His use of a banned substance (steroids) resulted in a two-year suspension from international competition and a lifetime ban from his national team. Clearly, his world-record performance will forever be viewed as artificial and tainted.

SPOTLIGHT ON STEROIDS

Steroid abuse was a topic at the 1984 National Strength and Conditioning Association's annual convention in Pittsburgh. One of the featured speakers was a world-class powerlifter who was also a self-admitted steroid user. During his presentation he remarked, "Why do people use steroids? I don't know — maybe they're tired of being wimps." The implication was that steroids will somehow make a person stronger and more desirable. Needless to say, the audience was incredulous. The speaker went on to recommend a product called Anabolic Mega-Pak as a nutritional alternative. The mention of this product brought mixed reactions ranging from raised eyebrows to suppressed laughter. Many people simply shook their heads in disbelief. (A month later, this particular product came under heavy scrutiny by the Federal Trade Commission for "engaging in deceptive acts and practices" and "disseminating false advertisements.") Shortly after a rather heated panel discussion on steroids, a small group of fitness professionals — myself included — approached the aforementioned powerlifter to question his previous use of steroids as to their subsequent effect on his health and his appropriateness as a role model for younger athletes. With a grin on his face, the individual stated, "I haven't used 100 milligrams a day in years!" (Generally, five milligrams is considered a therapeutic dose.) His years of heavy substance abuse were quite evident in his appearance — he looked nearly ten years older than his actual age and his eyeballs were yellowed from jaundice (a condition that results from diseased liver).

THE ABUSE OF STEROIDS

Steroid abuse is not a new problem. In fact, anabolic steroids may have first been used in World War II. It has been suspected that steroids were given to Nazi SS Troops to make them more aggressive and less fearful of violence. Athletes of Eastern Bloc countries were experimenting with steroids — or steroid-like drugs — as early as the 1950s. In a "patriotic" response to the drug-inspired success of the Soviet athletes at the 1956 Melbourne Olympics, U. S. Team Physician Dr. John Ziegler developed the original anabolic steroid (Dianabol) with Ciba Pharmaceutical Company . . . a move he would later regret. The steroids were given to weightlifters at the York Barbell Club in Pennsylvania who ate the pills "like candy." The rampant use of steroids, along with a new generation of growth-stimulating drugs, has been rising ever since.

Initially, steroids were used by competitive athletes who were looking to accelerate their gains in muscular size and strength with the hopes that this would improve their performance. This is still true, but steroid use has been reaching other populations as well. Perhaps the most disheartening information deals with the number of steroid users at the high school level. In a study out of Penn State, 3,403 twelfth-grade male students voluntarily completed a questionnaire concerning steroid use. The results indicate that 6.64% of twelfth-grade male students either use or have used steroids and that over two thirds of the user group initiated use when they were 16 years of age or younger. Extrapolating these data suggest that 250,000-500,000 adolescents are using or have used steroids. Such numbers are simply staggering. The study also revealed that approximately 20% of the users reported their source of steroids was a health-care professional (defined in this study as a physician, a pharmacist or — believe it or not — a veterinarian). Indeed, the use of steroids — and drugs in general — is reaching epidemic proportions.

WHAT ARE STEROIDS?

Technically referred to as being "anabolic-androgenic," steroids are synthetic derivatives of a powerful male sex hormone known as "testosterone." The "anabolic" or growth-promoting effects of testosterone include increases in skeletal muscle mass, nitrogen retention and protein synthesis while its "androgenic" or masculinizing effects include increases in facial and body hair, a deepening of the voice and a heightened libido. Steroids are derived from testosterone that has been chemically modified — primarily to enhance the anabolic effects and to decrease the androgenic effects. Steroids can be broadly categorized as those that are administered by either ingestion or injection.

RESEARCH FINDINGS

The following conclusions have been drawn from research studies concerning the use of steroids:

1. The administration of therapeutic doses of steroids to healthy individuals has not been shown in itself to elicit significant improvement in maximal strength, maximal oxygen uptake, aerobic performance, lean-body mass or bodyweight.

2. The research suggests that anabolic-steroid administration combined with resistance training results in an increased gain in bodyweight as compared to resistance training alone. However, the current data are inconclusive concerning the effects of anabolic-steroid adminis-

tration on body composition — that is, lean-body mass and percentage of body fat.

3. The research also suggests that anabolic-steroid administration combined with resistance training may increase maximal strength and/or power more than resistance training alone. Facilitation of strength development occurs most often in experienced weightlifters and may be the result of physiological or psychological changes.

Chapter 21
STEROID USE:
RISKS AND ETHICS

Scientific research data appear to be inconclusive regarding the effects of large doses or the long-term administration of anabolic steroids on the health — or improved physical abilities — of athletes. Although the long-term effects are unclear, the use of anabolic steroids does pose serious threats to the skin, kidneys, liver, testes and accessory sex glands as well as the cardiovascular, immune, endocrine, reproductive and skeletal systems thereby presenting dangers to overall health and longevity. In fact, Michigan State Strength Coach Ken Mannie says, "The list of adverse effects [from steroid use] reads like a Stephen King horror story." An examination of the "horror story" in greater detail will show you that this is no exaggeration.

POSSIBLE SIDE EFFECTS

It should also be noted that the potential for adverse side effects is a function of the type and amount of steroid being used as well as individual sensitivity. However, the adverse effects associated with the use of anabolic steroids occur quite frequently and many effects undoubtedly are not reported. The following is a list of the dangerous side effects that are well documented in the medical literature:

Mental Side Effects

These effects may include psychiatric disorders, severe depression, manic depression, paranoia, grandiose delusions, visual and auditory hallucinations, irritability, extreme mood swings that can be borderline psychotic and an abnormally high level of unpredictable hostility and aggression that is commonly referred to as "roid rage."

Physical/Physiological Side Effects

This may consist of hypertension (high blood pressure), cancerous tumors, cardiovascular dysfunction, kidney dysfunction, dermatologic syndromes (such as acne), insomnia, increased cholesterol levels, alopecia (loss of scalp hair), nosebleeds and a predisposition to tendon and ligament injuries. (Apparently, connective tissue does not respond to steroids to the same degree as muscle tissue. This creates a situation in which the connective tissue cannot keep up with the demands from using heavier weights. It has been likened to putting an engine from a Mack truck into a Volkswagen.)

There is also a possibility of various liver disorders such as peliosis hepatis (the pooling of blood in the liver), hepatoma (liver cancer) and jaundice. In addition, individuals also risk septic shock ("blood poisoning") and the spread of communicable diseases (including AIDS) from contaminated needles along with neural dysfunction as a result of improperly placed needles. Pre-mature fusing of the epiphyseal growth plates that results in stunted growth may occur in adolescents.

Wait, there's more: When a man starts to introduce extra testosterone into his body, then his body will reduce its own production in order to maintain a stable internal environment. If too much "foreign" testosterone is added, the body will no longer produce its own supply and the result is a feminizing effect. This chemical balancing can result in testicular atrophy (the testicles shrink), gynecomastia (the appearance of enlarged, female-like breasts on the male physique) and a high-pitched voice. If this bit of hormonal irony is not enough, males can also expect fluid retention, prostate enlargement, a decreased sperm count and functional impotency.

One more thing: Deaths have been directly — and legally — attributed to steroid use.

OVERT SIGNS OF STEROID USE

It is often difficult to identify the use of anabolic steroids. However, there are a few tell-tale signs. Because steroids can be taken orally in tablet/pill form or by direct injection into a muscle, users may have needles, syringes and pill bottles either hidden or in their possession. Steroid users often have puncture marks, bruises, scar tissue or calluses on their upper thighs and buttocks from steroid injections. Many physical indicators of steroid use are related to the adverse side effects. For example, steroid users often have a bloated, puffy look to their faces and skin due to fluid retention. Another physical sign is that the eyes and skin of a steroid user may have a somewhat yellowish tint from jaundice. Several other physical signs are an increased incidence of stretch marks, unprovoked nosebleeds, gynecomastia and severe acne (especially on the back). Finally, sudden and significant increases in size, weight and strength can also be signs of steroid use.

In terms of psychological signs, violent and unpredictable rage is a noticeable side effect of steroid use. Other indications of steroid use can be severe depression and an increased or decreased libido.

Just because one or two of these conditions are present does not necessarily indicate steroid use. However, if more than a few signs are present, you can bet that the individual is ingesting more than Flintstone vitamins.

WINNING AT ALL COSTS

Despite an incredible number of dangerous risks to overall health, evidence suggests that athletes will do anything — or take anything — to win. Personally, the desire to excel nearly drove me to use steroids. During my junior year at Penn State, I briefly considered using steroids because I needed to increase my lifts by about 10% in three months in order to qualify for the NCAA Powerlifting Championships. Though I ultimately chose to compete without any chemical substances, the temptation was great.

On the other hand, many people elect to take the "artificial" route to success. Dr. Gabe Mirkin once polled more than 100 top runners with this question: "If I could give you a pill that would make you an Olympic champion — and also kill you in a year — would you take it?" More than half of the athletes said that they would take the pill. Dr. Robert Goldman — a former collegiate wrestler and a co-author of *Death in the Locker Room* —

asked 198 elite athletes a similar question and again, more than half of those asked (52%) said, in effect, that they would give their lives to win. While some people's will to win can be applauded and admired, in this case it certainly contradicts the ideals of fair play of competition.

A MATTER OF ETHICS

Anabolic steroids do have some legitimate medical applications, such as in treating malnutrition, skeletal disorders, soft tissue injuries, recovery from surgery, osteoporosis and various anemias. However, the use of anabolic steroids in an attempt to improve physical capacity or athletic performance is contrary to the ethical principles and regulations of competitions as established and set down by various athletic foundations and sports-governing bodies. These organizations include the International Amateur Athletic Federation, the International Olympic Committee and the National Collegiate Athletic Association. Strong anti-steroid statements have also been issued by the American College of Sports Medicine, the National Strength and Conditioning Association and the National Football League.

STEROIDS AND THE LAW

The Anabolic Steroid Control Act of 1990 went into effect at the end of February 1991. Under this act, anabolic steroids are categorized as Schedule III drugs, which makes their use restricted in the same manner as some narcotics, depressants and stimulants. Legislation has penalties that include a maximal $1,000 fine and a maximal one-year sentence for possession (first offense) as well as a $250,000 fine and up to five years in prison for trafficking. The act gives federal drug-enforcement officials the authority to regulate manufacturers, wholesalers, doctors and pharmacies. It also allows for the seizure of assets and money earned through the trafficking of steroids.

A SOLUTION?

It is the duty of coaches, physical educators and parents to educate youths about all drugs and their potentially dangerous side effects. They must let youths know that drugs are not "the answer" whether it is for athletic performance or recreational use. Youths should be frequently reminded of the latest drug-related tragedies and that the use of controlled substances without a physician's approval is illegal. If youths are taking drugs illegally, it should be explained to them that the use of drugs as performance enhancers is unethical and immoral. Finally, the many long-term dangers associated with drug abuse should be emphasized.

Perhaps the most important (yet subtle) thing coaches, physical educators and parents can do for youths is to be good role models. Athletes and youths tend to copy certain characteristics, actions and even mannerisms of those whom they respect and admire. Therefore, it is imperative that those in authority talk, act and dress in a professional manner at all times in order to set as good an example as possible.

THE "SECRET" TO SUCCESS

I always smile whenever I read or hear about a secret training method, a miraculous fitness product or some other shortcut to success. Hey, there are no secret or mystical techniques for improving athletic ability — except maybe hard work and determination. If you give everything your best effort, things will work out for themselves. That does not only apply to the wrestling mat either — the same holds true for the classroom or anything with which you wish to be successful.

There are not any shortcuts on the road to success. The secret to becoming a better wrestler does not lie in a bottle, a pill or a syringe; success is measured by dedication, desire and effort. Remember, users are losers — you do not need drugs to be a winner!

BIBLIOGRAPHY

The following articles from *Wrestling USA* magazine (call 406-549-4448 for subscription information) were reprinted as chapters in this book:

Conventional Strength Training. vol 24, no 6 (January 15, 1989): 9-11.

A Practical Approach. vol 24, no 5 (December 15, 1988): 5-8.

The "Twenty Hour Rule": A Strength Coach's Perspective. vol 27, no 8 (March 1, 1992): 8-10.

Designing a Strength Program. vol 24, no 3 (October 15, 1988): 46-47.

Stimulating Muscular Growth. vol 23, no 4 (November 15, 1987): 14-15.

Fiber Types and Repetition Ranges. vol 33, no 10 (April 15, 1998): 9-10, 12.

Vary Your Workouts. vol 24, no 4 (November 15, 1988): 38-39.

Metabolic Conditioning—Part 1. vol 34, no 3 (October 15, 1998): 61-62.

Metabolic Conditioning—Part 2. vol 34, no 6 (January 15, 1999): 34-36.

The Pre-Exhaustion Principle: Bypassing the Weak Link. vol 33, no 8 (March 1, 1998): 43-44.

Getting the Most Out of Dips and Chins. vol 26, no 4 (November 15, 1990): 12.

Manual Resistance for Wrestlers. vol 23, no 6 (January 15, 1988): 24-25.

More Manual Resistance. vol 23, no 8 (March 1, 1988): 17-18.

Get a Grip! vol 35, no 3 (October 15, 1999): 8-11.

Barbell Squat. vol 36, no 4 (November 15, 2000): 12-13, 15.

Wrestling Camp. vol 36, no 2 (October 1, 2000): 20-21.

Improving Skills: What the Research Says. vol 35, no 4 (November 15, 1999): 8-11.

I Know What You Did Last Summer. vol 37, no 9 (March 15, 2002): 6-7.

Summer Conditioning Program for Wrestling. vol 21, no 7 (February 15, 1986): 5, 8-9.

Steroid Use: History and Prevalence. vol 27, no 1 (September 15, 1991): 70-71.

Steroid Use: Risks and Ethics. vol 27, no 2 (October 1, 1991): 12-14.

BIOGRAPHY

Matt Brzycki enlisted in the United States Marine Corps in June 1975. His active duty began two months later when he was sent to basic training (a.k.a. "boot camp") in Parris Island, South Carolina. When Mr. Brzycki completed his basic training in November 1975, he was presented the Leatherneck Award for achieving the highest score in rifle marksmanship in his platoon. In January 1978 — a little more than 28 months after beginning basic training — he was promoted meritoriously to the rank of sergeant. In May 1978, Mr. Brzycki entered Drill Instructor (DI) School at the Marine Corps Recruit Depot in San Diego, California. When he graduated from the school in August 1978 at the age of 21, he was one of the youngest DIs in the entire Marine Corps. Among his many responsibilities as a DI was the physical preparedness of Marine recruits. In August 1979, Mr. Brzycki was awarded a Certificate of Merit for successfully completing a tour of duty as a DI.

Shortly after his four-year enlistment ended in August 1979, Mr. Brzycki enrolled at Penn State. He earned a Bachelor of Science degree in Health and Physical Education in May 1983. Mr. Brzycki represented the university for two years in the Pennsylvania State Collegiate Powerlifting Championships (1981 and 1982) and was also a place-winner in his first bodybuilding competition (1981).

From May 1983-August 1984, Mr. Brzycki served as a Health Fitness Supervisor at Princeton University. In September 1984, he was named the Assistant Strength and Conditioning Coach at Rutgers University and remained in that position until July 1990. In August 1990, he returned to Princeton University as the school's Strength Coach and Health Fitness Coordinator. Mr. Brzycki was named the Coordinator of Health Fitness, Strength and Conditioning Programs in February 1994 (retroactive to December 1993). In March 2001, he was named the Coordinator of Recreational Fitness and Wellness Programming.

Over the years, Mr. Brzycki has worked with literally hundreds of male and female athletes in a wide variety of sports. Since November 1982, he has been involved in the strength and conditioning of collegiate wrestlers at three different schools: Penn State, Princeton University and Rutgers University.

Mr. Brzycki has taught at the collegiate level since 1990. He developed the Strength Training Theory and Applications course for Exercise Science and Sports Studies majors at Rutgers University and taught the program from March 1990-July 2000 as a member of the Faculty of Arts and Sciences. (Department of Exercise Science and Sport Studies.) He also taught the same course to Health and Physical Education majors at The College of New Jersey from January 1996-March 1999 as a member of the Health and Physical Education Faculty. All told, more than 600 university students in fitness-related majors took his courses in strength training for academic credit. Since September 1990, Mr. Brzycki has taught non-credit physical education courses at Princeton University including all of those pertaining to weight training.

Mr. Brzycki has been a featured speaker at local, regional, state and national conferences and clinics throughout the United States and Canada. Since November 1984, he has authored more than 200 articles on strength and fitness that have been featured in 36 different publications. Mr. Brzycki has written three books: *A Practical Approach to Strength Training* (1995), *Youth Strength and Conditioning* (1995) and *Cross Training for Fitness* (1997). He also co-authored *Conditioning for Basketball* (1993) with Shaun Brown who was, at the time, the Strength and Conditioning Coach for the University of Kentucky. (He is currently the Strength and Conditioning Coach for the Boston Celtics). Mr. Brzycki served as the editor of *Maximize your Training: Insights from Top Strength and Fitness Professionals* (1999). This 448-page book features the collective efforts of 37 leaders in the strength

111

and fitness profession. In 1997, he developed a correspondence course in strength training for Desert Southwest Fitness (Tucson, Arizona) that is used by strength and fitness professionals to update their certifications. The course has been approved and accepted for continuing education credits by 16 international organizations including the American Council on Exercise, the Australian Fitness Advisory Council, the International Fitness Professionals Association, the International Weightlifting Association and the National Federation of Professional Trainers.

In January 2001, Mr. Brzycki was named a Fellow at Forbes College (Princeton University). In April 2001, he was selected to serve on the Alumni Society Board of Directors for the College of Health & Human Development (Penn State). He and his wife, Alicia, reside in Lawrenceville, New Jersey, with their son, Ryan.

LEXILE LEVEL:
A.R. POINTS:
A.R. LEVEL: